13 Lessons in Christian Doctrine

Denver Sizemore
adapted by John Hunter

13
Lessons in
Christian
DOCTRINE

NIV Youth Edition

COLLEGE PRESS PUBLISHING COMPANY· JOPLIN, MISSOURI

International Standard Book Number: 0-89900-398-2

Preface

Denver Sizemore has graciously given permission to adapt his popular adult study, *13 Lessons in Christian Doctrine*. Many teachers and ministers across the country have used this book to teach basic principles of the faith for many years. Most recently, teachers have expressed their desire to have a similar study for young people. *13 Lessons in Christian Doctrine (NIV Youth Edition)* is presented to meet such a need. Wherever possible, Mr. Sizemore's wording has been left the same. The aim of this work has been to reword the text for both young people and new Christians. The workbook is intended to provide a tool for teaching basic Christian doctrine. The material at the close of each chapter may be used either as a review or a quiz.

Table Of Contents

God

Is there a God? What is he like? Does he care about us? What does he ask us to do? These are questions that everyone must face. The answers to these questions will set the direction for each of our lives.

I. How Do We Know There Is A God?

A. The Bible Says So

The Bible does not try to prove that there is a God. It simply states it as a fact. Turn to Genesis 1:1 to see what the very first verse in the Bible says (keep in mind that the quotations for this book are taken from the *New International Version-NIV*). Write the verse below:

_____

_____

Do you see that it claims that there is a God? It is simply stated as a fact! Turn to Psalm 14:1 and fill in the blanks: "The _____ says in his heart, 'There is _____ _____ .'" The Bible says that only a fool who does not know the facts would say there is no God! A fool does not say this for everyone to hear, but only to himself. The Bible is written with the belief that the proof for God is so strong that nobody should be able to say that there is no God.

But, for those people who will not believe what the Bible teaches about God, it is necessary to show added proof. Here are some more reasons for believing that there is a God:

B. Design in Creation Says So

When we look around us, we ask the question, "What caused this world?" There must have been a master mind behind it all! When we see a great house, we know that there must have been a wise builder. When we hear a beautiful song, we know there was a talented songwriter. When we look at this world, we know that there must have been a creator or designer. Here are some examples: The earth weighs over 6 million million billion tons! From one side of the earth to the other is 8,000 miles! To go all the way around the earth, you would have to travel

9

25,000 miles! The earth runs more smoothly than the finest watch. The earth travels over 595 million miles in a year as it moves around the sun. Yet, it does not change how long the trip takes by even one second! How can we explain this? There must have been a wise and powerful God who designed it all.

C. Nature Says So

Fill in the blanks from Psalm 19:1: "The _____ declare the _____ of God; the _____ proclaim the _____ of his hands." Paul says in Romans 1:20, "For since the creation of the world God's invisible qualities–his eternal nature–have been clearly seen, being understood from what has been made, so that men are without excuse." As we look at the world about us, we can be sure there is a God and that he is powerful and wise. Answer "yes" or "no" to this question: Do people who refuse to believe this have any excuse? _____

D. The Heart Says So

Man knows in his heart that there is a higher being. He desires to worship him. This is true of even the most pagan tribes of people. Paul found this true at Athens. (Turn to Acts 17:23 and fill in the blanks): "For as I walked around and looked carefully at your objects of _____, I even found an altar with this inscription: TO AN _____ GOD. Now what you _____ as something _____ I am going to proclaim to you." Where did man get this knowledge of God? The animals do not know it. Man alone in all creation is a "religious" being. This knowledge was placed within man by his designer, God. The person who says there is no God is not able to explain this sense of God any other way!

II. What Are Some Names For God?

The most common name for God in the Old Testament is "Jehovah." This means the "Living One." The question is often asked, "Where did God come from?" The answer is that he didn't come from anywhere or anyone else! He is alive within himself and always has been alive. We find this hard to understand. When Moses asked God for his name in Exodus 3:14, he said, "I AM WHO I AM. This is what you are to say to the Israelites: 'I AM has sent me to you.'" This is another way of saying "Jehovah"– the "Living One." This name clearly means that God has lived forever.

The name "Elohim" (Eh-lo-heem) is used for God in Genesis 1:1, "In the beginning God created the heavens and the earth." It is the name used often in the rest of the Old Testament. The name means "the Strong One." This is another way of saying that he is all-powerful. We can especially see this in the creation story.

"Adon" is another name used for God. It means "Lord" or "Master." This name is used for God many times in the Bible. Again we can see that God has all power over man and his creation. Explain in your own words what these names for God mean:

1. "Jehovah"

_____

_____

2. "Elohim"

_____

_____

3. "Adon"

_____

_____

III. What Is God Like?

What we can see in this world tells us that there is a God. The Bible— God's way of telling us about himself—tells us what he is like. Here is a list of a few of the many ways that he is special:

A. He Is One God

There is one God (Turn to Deuteronomy 6:4 and fill in the missing words): "_____,O Israel: The _____ our God, the _____ is _____ ." God is three persons! There is God the Father, God the Son and God the Holy Spirit. The word "God" is used for each of these "persons" in the Bible. Read 1 Corinthians 8:6; John 1:1; and Acts 5:3, 4. Write below what you learn about God from these verses.

_____

_____

_____

_____

This idea of three persons for one God seems strange to us. But it does not seem to be a problem for the ones who wrote the New Testament. They believed it by a trusting faith in God. In a similar way, man has three parts. Although man is not three persons like God, he still may be said to have: "spirit, soul, and body" (See 1 Thessalonians 5:23). Man is a spirit with a soul and lives in a body. Man still thinks of himself as one person! No one really understands how this can be. We may not understand how God can be three persons either. We simply accept God's word by faith.

B. He Is Holy

This is one of the greatest differences between God and all the false gods created by man. The gods that man has created are full of sin and weak—just like their creators! When man creates a god, he makes sure that his new god does not punish him for his sin. This is not true about Jehovah. Israel was surrounded by people who worshiped false gods. These false gods were unholy. Jehovah spoke so all could hear, "Speak to the entire assembly of Israel and say to them: 'Be holy because I, the LORD your God, am holy.'" (Leviticus 19:2). The prophet Isaiah saw a vision in the temple of the Lord and his angels calling to one another, "Holy, holy, holy is the LORD Almighty; the whole earth is full of his glory" (Isaiah 6:3). In Jesus' example of how to pray, the first words are, "'Our Father in heaven, hallowed [holy] be your name'"(Matthew 6:9). In your own words, tell what it means to keep God's name "holy":

_____
_____
_____
_____

Because God is holy, he hates everything that is full of sin and evil. He loves everything that is pure, good, and holy. David sang to God in the Psalms, "The arrogant cannot stand in your presence; you hate all who do wrong" (Psalm 5:5). It is because God is holy that he cannot be tempted by evil. He cannot sin. Turn to James 1:13 and fill in the blanks: "When _____, no one should say, '_____ is _____ me.' For _____ cannot be _____ by evil, nor does he _____ anyone."

A woman dressed in a white satin dress hates dirt much more than a ditch digger does. The cleaner a person becomes in his soul, the more he hates sin! Since God is completely holy, he has a burning hatred for all evil. God destroyed the world once by the flood. He will destroy the world once and for all by fire. Both of these show how God feels about sin because of his holiness.

The word "saint" in the New Testament means a "holy one." Every child of God who is living a holy life is a saint. As children of a holy God we are called upon to live like him. 1 Peter 1:14-16 says, "As obedient children, do not conform to the evil desires you had when you lived in ignorance. But just as he who called you is holy, so be holy in all you do; for it is written: 'Be holy, because I am holy.'" In your own words explain what a "saint" is:

_____

_____

_____

C. He Is Love

This is the supreme picture of what God is like. John tells us, "Whoever does not love does not know God, because God is love" (1 John 4:8). Love comes the closest to describing what God is like. Love is the reason that sent Jesus to save lost people! Turn to John 3:16,17 and fill in the missing words: "For God so _____ the world that he gave his one and only _____, that whoever _____ in him shall not perish but have _____ _____. For God did not send his _____ into the world to _____ the world, but to _____ the world through him."

The love of God for people is first seen when God sent Jesus to earth to save us. 1 John 4:9, 10 says, "This is how God showed his love among us: He sent his one and only Son into the world that we might live through him. This is love: not that we loved God, but that he loved us and sent his Son as an atoning sacrifice for our sins." His love is also seen in the fact that he has made us his sons when we obey the Good News. His love is higher than any love man can have. (Turn to Romans 5:6-8. Explain how God shows his love for us. Fill in the lines that follow.)

_____

_____

His love is also seen in how he cares for the world. He especially cares for his saints! (See Matthew 5:44-48 and Romans 8:28.)

His forgiveness of our sins over and over again shows how much he loves us. King Hezekiah said, "Surely it was for my benefit that I suffered such anguish. In your love you kept me from the pit of destruction; you have put all my sins behind your back" (Isaiah 38:17).

God's love for us causes us to love him. "We love because he first loved us" (1 John 4:19). His love can move us to love one another. 1 John 4:11 says, "we also

13

ought to love one another." (See also John 14:15.)

D. He Is Full of Mercy

God's love is why he has mercy. Paul says, "But because of his great love for us, God, who is rich in mercy, made us alive with Christ even when we were dead in transgressions—it is by grace you have been saved. And God raised us up with Christ and seated us with him in the heavenly realms in Christ Jesus, in order that in the coming ages he might show the incomparable riches of his grace, expressed in his kindness to us in Christ Jesus" (Ephesians 2:4-7).

Three great words are used together often in the Bible: love, mercy and grace. *Love* is why he has *mercy*. God gives *grace* because he is full of mercy!
God shows his mercy daily when we are truly sorry for the wrong things we have done and ask for forgiveness. Turn to 2 Peter 3:9 to fill in the missing words: The Lord is "_____ _____ in keeping his promise, as some understand _____. He is _____ with you, not wanting anyone to _____, but everyone to come to _____."
How wonderful is His mercy!

E. He Is All-Powerful

God says in Genesis 17:1, "I am God Almighty; walk before me and be blameless." There is no limit to his power. In Revelation 19:6, the people said, "Hallelujah! For our Lord God Almighty reigns." With this unlimited power God created the world in the beginning and keeps it going! The miracles of the Bible were performed because of God's power. Men have a hard time believing the story of creation in Genesis and the miracles in the Bible. They do not believe that God is All-Powerful. Once Jesus explained to a rich young man what it meant to be saved, "With man this is impossible, but with God all things are possible" (Matthew 19:26).

Explain in your own words what it means for God to be "All-Powerful":
_____
_____
_____

F. He Is All-Knowing

Paul sings a song of praise about God's wisdom in Romans 11:33, "Oh, the depth of the riches of the wisdom and knowledge of God! How unsearchable his judgments, and his paths beyond tracing out!" "Great is our Lord and mighty in power;

his understanding has no limit" (Psalm 147:5).

God's knowledge is so great that he knows little things as well as great things. Jesus says he sees the sparrow fall and knows that the very hairs of our head are all numbered (Matthew 10:30). John writes, "This then is how we know that we belong to the truth, and how we set our hearts at rest in his presence whenever our hearts condemn us. For God is greater than our hearts, and he knows everything" (1 John 3:19, 20).

He knows all about us, even our thoughts. "O LORD, you have searched me and you know me. You know when I sit and when I rise; you perceive my thoughts from afar. You discern my going out and my lying down; you are familiar with all my ways. Before a word is on my tongue you know it completely, O LORD" (Psalm 139:1-4).

Explain in your own words what it means for God to be "All-Knowing":

_____

_____

_____

G. He Is Everywhere

Being spirit, God can be everywhere. He is always present. "'Am I only a God nearby,' declares the LORD, 'and not a God far away? Can anyone hide in secret places so that I cannot see him?'" (Jeremiah 23:23,24). David could not think of a place where he could go and not find God's love and care. We are never far from God as Paul told the non-believing people in Athens, "God did this so that men would seek him and perhaps reach out for him and find him, though he is not far from each one of us. 'For in him we live and move and have our being.' As some of your own poets have said, 'We are his offspring.'" (Acts 17:27,28).

God is not limited by time because he is eternal. He is not limited in power because he is all-powerful. He is all-knowing. He is not limited in knowledge. He is everywhere. He is not limited by any space! Deuteronomy 10:17 says, "For the LORD your God is God of gods and Lord of lords, the great God, mighty and awesome, who shows no partiality and accepts no bribes."

H. He Is Faithful

"Know therefore that the LORD your God is God; he is the faithful God, keeping his covenant of love to a thousand generations of those who love him and keep his commands" (Deuteronomy 7:9).

Constant change in every area of life makes it seem like nothing is stable. But God is not this way! The things of this world do change. God does not change. David said, "In the beginning you laid the foundations of the earth, and the heavens are the work of your hands. They will perish, but you remain; they will all wear out like a garment. Like clothing you will change them and they will be discarded. But you remain the same, and your years will never end" (Psalm 102:25-27).

God is faithful because he does not change! Jehovah said, "I the LORD do not change" (Malachi 3:6). God's ways of doing things may change. But who he *is* does not change. Because God does not change, people can trust his promises. He is also faithful because he is powerful. People sometimes do not keep their promises because they are weak. God can do anything he promises to do! Hebrews 10:23 says, "Let us hold unswervingly to the hope we profess, for he who promised is faithful."

Explain in your own words what it means for God to be "Faithful":

_____

_____

_____

IV. How Do We Know And Obey God?

As we think about how great God is, we can agree with Jeremiah 9:23,24, "This is what the LORD says: 'Let not the wise man boast of his wisdom or the strong man boast of his strength or the rich man boast of his riches, but let him who boasts boast about this: that he understands and knows me, that I am the LORD, who exercises kindness, justice and righteousness on earth, for in these I delight,' declares the LORD." In your own words, explain what these verses mean:

_____

_____

_____

Our highest goal in life should be: "Now all has been heard; here is the conclusion of the matter: Fear God and keep his commandments, for this is the whole duty of man" (Ecclesiastes 12:13).

God

Answer True Or False:

_____ **1.** Man has no knowledge of God except for the Bible.

_____ **2.** Everywhere present means "not limited to a specific place."

_____ **3.** God never changes.

_____ **4.** The gods that people create are powerful and holy.

_____ **5.** The New Testament teaches us that everyone is a saint.

Fill In The Blanks:

John 3:16,17: "For God so _____ the world that he gave his one and only _____, that whoever_____ in him shall not _____ , but have _____ _____. For God did not send his _____ into the world to _____ the world, but to save the world through him."

Psalm 102:25-27: "In the _____ you laid the _____ of the earth, and the _____ are the work of your _____. They will _____, but you _____; they will all wear out like a garment. Like clothing you will _____ them and they will be discarded. But you _____ the same, and your years will never end."

Jesus, The Christ

"She will give birth to a son, and you are to give him the name Jesus, because he will save his people from their sins" (Matthew 1:21). The angel of the Lord told Joseph about Jesus, his name and his mission. Jesus is the Greek name for the Hebrew word "Joshua"—it means "Jehovah is salvation." Jesus means "Savior." This name describes his work of saving people from their sins (see Luke 19:10). The name "Christ" or "Messiah" means "chosen one." It names Jesus as the One who was to come as promised in the Old Testament. The two names together, Jesus Christ, mean that he is the Messiah who came to earth to save lost people! Answer the following questions in your own words.

What was Jesus' name in Hebrew? _____

What did his Hebrew name mean? _____

What does the name "Christ" mean? _____

I. Jesus Is The Son Of God

Who is this Jesus, the Messiah? Many answers have been given. Some of the Jews thought he was only the son of Mary and Joseph (see Mark 6:3 and Matthew 13:55). Others called him a liar (see Matthew 27:63). Still others thought that he was a prophet. Write John 6:14 in the blanks.

_____

_____

Some people today say that Jesus is just a man. He only lived a better life than anyone else did. What does the Bible say? What did key leaders say? What did Jesus say? What did his apostles say about who he was?

1. John the Baptist said that Jesus is the Son of God. "I have seen and I testify that this is the Son of God" (John 1:34).

2. Mark said that Jesus is the Son of God. "The beginning of the gospel about Jesus Christ, the Son of God" (Mark 1:1).

3. Peter said that Jesus is the Son of God. "Simon Peter answered, "You are the Christ, the Son of the living God'" (Matthew 16:16).

4. Paul said that Jesus is the Son of God. "But when the time had fully come, God sent his Son, born of a woman, born under law" (Galatians 4:4).

19

5. The angel Gabriel said that Jesus is the Son of God. "The angel answered, 'The Holy Spirit will come upon you, and the power of the Most High will overshadow you. So the holy one to be born will be called the Son of God'" (Luke 1:35).

6. The demons said that Jesus is the Son of God. "'What do you want with us, Son of God?' they shouted. 'Have you come here to torture us before the appointed time?'" (Matthew 8:29).

7. Jesus himself said that he is the Son of God. "But Jesus remained silent and gave no answer. Again the high priest asked him, 'Are you the Christ, the Son of the Blessed One?' 'I am,' said Jesus. 'And you will see the Son of Man sitting at the right hand of the Mighty One and coming on the clouds of heaven'" (Mark 14:61, 62).

8. God said that Jesus is his Son. And a voice from heaven said, "This is my Son, whom I love; with him I am well pleased" (Matthew 3:17; see also Matthew 17:5).

Jesus has special godly powers, and honors were given to him. Besides the eight witnesses to who Jesus is, he has special powers and honors that only belong to God. List the eight witnesses that said Jesus is the Son of God:

1. _____   5. _____

2. _____   6. _____

3. _____   7. _____

4. _____   8. _____

Christ has the power to create. Throughout the Bible only God has the power to create. Look up these verses and see that Jesus has this power! (John 1:1-3; Ephesians 3:8-11; and Colossians 1:16,17). Choose one of those Scriptures and put it in your own words:

_____

_____

_____

_____

Jesus has the power to forgive sins. Only God has this power! Luke 5:20-25 shows that Jesus has the power to forgive sin when he healed the crippled man.

Christ is to be worshiped. Only God is to be worshiped. This honor is given to Jesus by the Father. Look up John 5:22,23 and fill in the missing words: "Moreover, the Father _____ no one, but has entrusted all _____ to the Son, that all may _____ the Son just as they_____ the Father. He who does not _____ the Son does not _____ the Father, who sent him."

These powers and honors are Christ's because he is "the only Son" of God. God has chosen to give these things to him. Jesus was not only a man. He is the only Son of God. He came to earth and lived as a man for a few years. But he is and always has been in a special sense God's only Son.

II. Names That Tell Who Jesus Is And What He Does

Someone has counted 254 different names given for Jesus in the Bible. Jesus may be compared to a diamond. A diamond has many sides. Each side will show a new and beautiful side of the diamond. Like a diamond, you can look at Jesus in different ways and see new and beautiful things about him. In this lesson, we will look at a few of those sides or ways of seeing Jesus and what he does.

A. Jesus Is Our Savior

Webster's Dictionary defines "Savior" as "one who saves or delivers." This side of Jesus' life is the brightest side of all. The angel told Joseph, "You are to give him the name Jesus, because he will save his people from their sins" (Matthew 1:21). The angel of the Lord also told the shepherds on the hill, "Today in the town of David a Savior has been born to you; he is Christ the Lord" (Luke 2:11). Look up Luke 19:10 and tell what Jesus said his mission would be:

_____

_____

_____

_____

_____

Romans 5:6-8 says that man was weak and not able to save himself. Man was a sinner and did not deserve to be saved. But by the grace and love of God, Christ died to save him! 1 Peter 1:18,19 tells us that we have been bought with something more valuable than money. "For you know that it was not with perishable things such as silver or gold that you were redeemed from the empty way of life handed down to you from your forefathers, but with the precious blood of Christ, a lamb without blemish or defect." The great promise of Christianity is that God in his love for man saved us. Fill in the missing words from Titus 3:5,6: "he _____ us, not because of _____ things we had done, but because of his _____. He saved us through the _____ of rebirth and renewal by the Holy Spirit, whom he poured out on us generously through _____ _____ our Savior." Only Christianity has a Savior. This is another reason that it is the only true religion.

B. Jesus Is Our Lord

No name used by the early believers describes their faith better than calling Jesus "Lord." Peter spoke on the Day of Pentecost that the Jews had killed Jesus on the cross. "God has made this Jesus, whom you crucified, both Lord and Christ" (Acts 2:36). In Acts 10:36, Peter says he is "Lord of all."

Paul says, "if you confess with your mouth 'Jesus is Lord,' and believe in your heart that God raised him from the dead, you will be saved" (Romans 10:9). The believer confesses Jesus as his Savior, as his Christ and as his Lord! In Philippians 2:9-11, Paul explains that "God exalted him to the highest place and gave him the name that is above every name, that at the name of Jesus every knee should bow, in heaven and on earth and under the earth, and every tongue confess that Jesus Christ is Lord, to the glory of God the Father."

The name "Lord" tells us that Christ is in charge. He is in charge over his church (see Colossians 1:18). He is the Master, the Christian is his servant. The name "Savior" tells us what Christ has done and is doing for believers. The name "Lord" should tell us how we should live for him. Many people love to hear and read what Jesus has done for them. But often they do not care what Christ wants them to do in return. If Christ is not Lord of all, he will not be our Lord at all! Jesus said, "Why do you call me, 'Lord, Lord,' and do not do what I say?" (Luke 6:46). Christians need to hear this today.

C. Jesus Is Our Go-Between

A "go-between" is a person who tries to make peace between two people who are fighting. The Bible teaches that man is an enemy of God because of sin. People are separated from God because of sin. When we are enemies of God, lfe seems hopeless!

Christ came and died that he might make peace between God and man. He came to make peace for Jews and non-Jews! Fill in the missing words from Ephesians 2:14-16: "He himself is our _____, who has made the two one and has _____ the barrier, the dividing wall of hostility, by abolishing in his _____ the law with its commandments and regulations. His purpose was to _____ in himself one new man out of the two, thus making peace, and in this one body to reconcile both of them to God through the _____, by which he put to death their hostility."

Christ died on the cross in order to take away the great wall between God and man—sin. By accepting Jesus' forgiveness through the Good News, people can become friends with God again! Only Christ could remove this wall of sin. Christ had

22

no sin. No one could die for someone else's sin, unless he had no sin. Only Jesus could be the go-between for God and man. Paul told Timothy "For there is one God and one mediator between God and men, the man Christ Jesus, who gave himself as a ransom for all men—the testimony given in its proper time"(1 Timothy 2:5,6). Jesus said, "No one comes to the Father except through me" (John 14:6).

A go-between should know both sides and care for the good of everyone. Jesus came to earth to show people that he cared to understand man's problem of sin. He already knew how God loved people. He came to love us as God does (see Hebrews 2:17,18 and 4:15,16). Explain what the following mean about Jesus:

"Lord"_____

"Savior"_____

"Go-Between" _____

D. Jesus Is Our Prophet

The work of Jesus is divided into three jobs: king, priest and prophet. The prophet in the Old Testament was a man who spoke for God. Amos said he was not a trained prophet. "I was neither a prophet nor a prophet's son, but I was a shepherd, and I also took care of sycamore-fig trees. But the LORD took me from tending the flock and said to me, 'Go, prophesy to my people Israel'" (Amos 7:14,15). The prophets spoke God's message for their time and need. They also predicted things to happen in the future. The Old Testament points to one prophet who would come to be God's spokesman on earth. In Deuteronomy 18:15, Moses said that "The LORD your God will raise up for you a prophet like me from your own brothers. You must listen to him." Peter tells us that this prophet was Jesus (see Acts 3:19-26). Hebrews 1:1,2 says that God spoke to people in many ways, but "in these last days he has spoken to us by his Son, whom he appointed heir of all things, and through whom he made the universe." Jesus came to be the teacher that would tell people about God's will.

As God's prophet, Jesus spoke for God. "When Jesus had finished saying these things, the crowds were amazed at his teaching, because he taught as one who had authority, and not as their teachers of the law" (Matthew 7:28,29). He spoke in simple words and clearly so that all men could understand. Mark 12:37 says, "The large crowd listened to him with delight." Everyone, including his enemies, said, "No one ever spoke the way this man does" (John 7:46).

What did Jesus tell his disciples the night before he died? (John 14:26)

_____

_____

When we read the New Testament we can accept it with faith and be sure that it is God's message for us. Jesus, God's great prophet, has said, "My teaching is not my own. It comes from him who sent me" (John 7:16). And, in John 8:38, "I am telling you what I have seen in the Father's presence, and you do what you have heard from your father."

E. Jesus Is Our High Priest

A priest in the past was a minister or a leader of a religion. The high priest was the leader of the priests. In Hebrews, Jesus is called our high priest ten times. Christ is pictured as the true high priest. All the other high priests until Jesus were pointing to the time when Jesus would be the last high priest. What does 1 Peter 2:9 say that we are?

_____

_____

_____

Hebrews 5:1 explains what a high priest did: "Every high priest is selected from among men and is appointed to represent them in matters related to God, to offer gifts and sacrifices for sins." The job of the high priest under the law was to lead the worship of God in the Temple. He also offered the sacrifices to God for all the people. Aaron, brother of Moses, had to offer sacrifices first for himself, then for the rest of the people. He had to do this because he was a human being like all the others. Aaron would then go back a second time into the Most Holy Place and sprinkle blood on the ark of the covenant. This was for the sins of all the people in Israel (see Hebrews 9:1-10). John the Baptist spoke of Jesus as "the Lamb of God, who takes away the sin of the world!" (John 1:29). In Hebrews 10:1-7, Jesus is the one who was the perfect sacrifice for sins.

Jesus was chosen by God to be the high priest. "No one takes this honor upon himself; he must be called by God, just as Aaron was. So Christ also did not take upon himself the glory of becoming a high priest. But God said to him, 'You are my Son; today I have become your Father.' And he says in another place, 'You are a priest forever, in the order of Melchizedek'" (Hebrews 5:4-6).

Jesus was prepared by God to be the high priest. Jesus left the glory of heaven to come to earth and become a man. (See Philippians 2:5-8.)

Hebrews 4:15 tells us, "For we do not have a high priest who is unable to sympathize with our weaknesses, but we have one who has been tempted in every way, just as we are—yet was without sin." Jesus is the perfect one to be our high priest before the Father. Fill in the missing words from Hebrews 2:17,18: "For this reason

24

he had to be made like his _____ in every way, in order that he might become a _____ and faithful high priest in _____ to God, and that he might make atonement for the _____ of the people. Because he himself _____ when he was tempted, he is able to _____ those who are being tempted." Jesus is still our high priest to God and is able to help us to be forgiven of our sins.

When Jesus offered himself as our sacrifice, he did something that all the other sacrifices could not do. His death on the cross was once for all time. He brought an end to animal sacrifices for sin. Jesus was the last sacrifice. He put sin away forever. He made it possible to have eternal life through the blood he gave on the cross.

F. Jesus Is Our King

Jeremiah prophesied that Jesus would be a king. Jeremiah 23:5 says, "'The days are coming,' declares the LORD, 'when I will raise up to David a righteous Branch, a King who will reign wisely and do what is just and right in the land.'"

Jesus became king because God said that he would be a king. He was born into the kingly family of David through Mary and Joseph. Write what Gabriel told Mary in Luke 1:32:

_____

_____

_____

_____

God promised David that one would come in the future to set up a kingdom forever. (See 2 Samuel 7:12,13.) This is just what Jesus did!

Jesus claimed that he was a king. After he was baptized he told that the kingdom of heaven was near. In Matthew 16:28 he said, "I tell you the truth, some who are standing here will not taste death before they see the Son of Man coming in his kingdom." When Jesus was on trial before Pilate, Jesus was asked if he was the king of the Jews. "'Yes, it is as you say,' replied Jesus" (Luke 23:3).

Jesus has a spiritual kingdom. In John 18:36, Jesus said, "My kingdom is not of this world. If it were, my servants would fight to prevent my arrest by the Jews. But now my kingdom is from another place." Romans 14:17 explains what Jesus meant, "For the kingdom of God is not a matter of eating and drinking, but of righteousness, peace and joy in the Holy Spirit."

Explain what the following mean about Jesus:

"Prophet" _____

"Priest" _____

"King" _____

Jesus will rule forever. God told Mary through the angel Gabriel that Jesus would rule forever (see Luke 1:33). 2 Peter 1:11 says, "and you will receive a rich welcome into the eternal kingdom of our Lord and Savior Jesus Christ."

Jesus, The Christ

Answer True Or False:

_____ **1.** The name "Jesus" means "Savior."

_____ **2.** Jesus did not say he was the Son of God.

_____ **3.** The name "Lord" was used by Jesus only when he was here.

_____ **4.** A "Go-Between" is a person who makes peace between people who are fighting.

_____ **5.** A "prophet" is a person who speaks for God.

_____ **6.** Jesus is a prophet like Moses was.

_____ **7.** The main job of the high priest was to offer sacrifices.

_____ **8.** Jesus was a high priest exactly like the ones in the Old Testament.

_____ **9.** Prophets in the Old Testament told about the future.

_____ **10.** Jesus will be king forever.

Fill In The Blanks:

1. Write two powers that God and Christ both have:

a. _____

b. _____

2. How were the Old Testament high priests and Jesus different? List three ways on the blanks below:

a. _____

b. _____

c. _____

The Bible

The Bible is the most amazing book in the world. Thomas Carlyle said, "I call the Bible, apart from all theories about it, one of the greatest things ever written with pen. A noble book! All man's book!"

It is *the* best-selling book in the world! For the past 100 years, 2 million copies have been sold every year! It has been translated into over 2,000 languages. This is more than any other book!

I. The Bible Has Different Names

The word "Bible" itself means "book." Many religions have their collection of holy writings, sometimes called "bibles." When Christians use the word "Bible," they mean the Old and New Testaments. It is the written authority for the Christian faith. The Bible has other names for itself.

A. The Word of God

"And we also thank God continually because, when you received the word of God, which you heard from us, you accepted it not as the word of men, but as it actually is, the word of God, which is at work in you who believe" (1 Thessalonians 2:13). 1 Peter 1:23 says that we have been born again "through the living and enduring word of God." This tells us that the Bible is the message or "word" which comes from God.

B. Living Commands or Teachings From God

Stephen talked about the law given to Moses on Mount Sinai, "he received living words to pass on to us" (Acts 7:38). God's commands are living messages from the living God. Paul calls the Old Testament God's "very words" (Romans 3:2). Moses told the children of Israel to keep the teachings of God and to teach their children to keep them too. "They are not just idle words for you—they are your life. By them you will live long in the land you are crossing the Jordan to possess" (Deuteronomy 32:47).

C. The Holy Scriptures

Paul calls the Old Testament "the Holy Scriptures" (Romans 1:2). Turn to 2 Timothy 3:15 and write what Paul told Timothy:

_____

_____

_____

Scriptures are writings of God. Look up other verses that talk about "the Scriptures" (Matthew 21:42; Mark 14:49; Luke 24:32; John 5:39; Acts 18:24; Romans 15:4). Choose one of these Scriptures and write it here:

_____

_____

_____

II. How The Bible Began

A. What the Bible Says About Itself

1. *The Old Testament*

Several hundred times the writers of the Old Testament used the words "the LORD said" (Exodus 24:12, 25:1; Ezekiel 5:5,11). David says in 2 Samuel 23:2, "The Spirit of the LORD spoke through me; his word was on my tongue." When Jeremiah was called to be a prophet he said, "Then the LORD reached out his hand and touched my mouth and said to me, 'Now I have put my words in your mouth.'" (Jeremiah 1:9).

The apostle Paul spoke about the Old Testament to Timothy, "All Scripture is God-breathed and is useful for teaching, rebuking, correcting and training in righteousness, so that the man of God may be thoroughly equipped for every good work" (2 Timothy 3:16,17).

The apostle Peter tells us that the prophets in the Old Testament did not create their own message. Write 2 Peter 1:21 in the blanks:

_____

_____

_____

Jesus' apostles always thought of the Old Testament as the message from God.

The writers of the New Testament also claimed that their message came from God. Paul says in Galatians 1:11,12, "I want you to know, brothers, that the gospel I preached is not something that man made up. I did not receive it from any man, nor was I taught it; rather, I received it by revelation from Jesus Christ."

Peter spoke of Paul's writings as if they were Scripture, equal with the Old Testament, as being from God. "Bear in mind that our Lord's patience means salvation, just as our dear brother Paul also wrote you with the wisdom that God gave him. He writes the same way in all his letters, speaking in them of these matters. His letters contain some things that are hard to understand, which ignorant and unstable people distort, as they do the other Scriptures, to their own destruction" (2 Peter 3:15,16). The Holy Spirit was promised to help Jesus' apostles remember what they were taught (John 14:26; Matthew 10:19,20). Paul praised the Christians at Thessalonica because they believed that his message came from God. (Fill in the missing words from 1 Thessalonians 2:13): "And we also thank God continually because, when you received the _____ of God, which you _____ from us, you accepted it not as the _____ of men, but as it actually is, the _____ of God, which is at work in you who believe."

The whole Bible claims that God is its author. The message was written by men with the help of the Holy Spirit.

B. Other Proof That the Bible Came From God

1. *Prophecies that have come true*

This is one of the best proofs that the Bible came from God. The prophets would predict that something would happen hundreds of years into the future. When it really happened the way that they said, it showed they were from God.

Here are some of the prophecies about Jesus that show that the Bible is from God:

	Prophecy	Fulfilled
a. Place of Jesus' birth	Micah 5:2	Luke 2:1-7
b. John the Baptist	Isaiah 40:3	Matthew 3:1-3
c. Handed over to enemies	Psalm 41:9	John 13:18
d. Died with sinners	Isaiah 53:9	Luke 23:33
e. Not a bone broken	Psalm 34:20	John 19:31-37
f. Buried by a rich man	Isaiah 53:9	Matt. 27:57-60
g. Jesus' resurrection	Psalm 16:10	Matt. 28:1-6

31

2. *Its wonderful unity*

The Bible was written over 1,500 years by at least 40 people. These people were shepherds, kings, farmers and doctors. The Bible was written in three different languages (Hebrew, Aramaic and Greek). The 66 separate books on every subject you can think of form one book! How can this be humanly possible? Only God could have caused this kind of unity!

III. The Bible Is Valuable

How important is the Bible to people? How important is it to the unsaved? Christians know that it is the most important book anyone can read. This is true for both the saved and the unsaved.

A. It Has Value to the Unsaved

The Bible says:

1. *We are born by the word.*

"For you have been born again, not of perishable seed, but of imperishable, through the living and enduring word of God" (1 Peter 1:23). James 1:18 says, "He chose to give us birth through the word of truth, that we might be a kind of first-fruits of all he created."

2. *We are saved by the word.*

James 1:21: "Therefore, get rid of all moral filth and the evil that is so prevalent and humbly accept the word planted in you, which can save you."

3. *Faith comes through the word.*

What does Paul say in Romans 10:17?

_____

_____

_____

We know that Christ is the one who saves us. The Bible is the source of our knowledge of Jesus. We read in the Bible how he saves us. Without the word there would be no knowledge of his love. There would be no faith or obedience on our part. This is why the Bible says that we are saved through the word. This is

32

the way that God brings us to Christ.

B. It Has Value to the Saved

The Bible is vital to Christians. There are many ways that the Bible is vital for the Christian. It helps us grow spiritually. Turn to 1 Peter 2:2 and write the verse:

_____

_____

The Bible is like food for the spiritual man. Jesus said, "It is written: 'Man does not live on bread alone, but on every word that comes from the mouth of God'" (Matthew 4:4). When we do not study the Bible we become weak. Paul told the elders of the Ephesian church, "Now I commit you to God and to the word of his grace, which can build you up and give you an inheritance among all those who are sanctified" (Acts 20:32).

Believers are made clean from the "dirt" of sin by the word of God. Jesus told his apostles, "You are already clean because of the word I have spoken to you" (John 15:3). We know that it is the blood of Jesus which makes us clean from all sin (see 1 John 1:7 and Hebrews 9:14). It is through the word that we come to know about his blood. David asked this question and gave the answer. Turn to Psalm 119:9 and answer the question, "How can a young person live a pure life?"

_____

_____

_____

The word is the way we can keep clean and be set apart for God's use. This is another way of saying that we are "saints." Jesus prayed in John 17:17, "Sanctify them by the truth; your word is truth."

Someone once said, "This Book will keep you from sin, or sin will keep you from this Book."

By the word of God, Christians are able to face the attacks of the devil. When the devil tempted Jesus in the desert, Jesus was able to answer him with the word of God. (See Matthew 4:1-11. Write in your own words how Jesus used the Bible to answer the devil.)

_____

_____

Paul told the Ephesians, "Put on the full armor of God so that you can take your stand against the devil's schemes. Take the helmet of salvation and the sword of the Spirit, which is the word of God" (Ephesians 6:11 and 17). The Bible is the Christian's sword to fight the spiritual battle against the devil. David says, "I have hidden your word in my heart that I might not sin against you" (Psalm 119:11).

IV. How To Read And Understand The Bible

Our God is a God of wisdom. His Bible is a book of knowledge. God always invites people to come to him now. "'Come now, let us reason together,' says the LORD. 'Though your sins are like scarlet, they shall be as white as snow; though they are red as crimson, they shall be like wool'" (Isaiah 1:18). Since this is true, we should read the Bible like we would read a book of knowledge.

Here are some ways to help us study the Bible. They will help make it easy to understand.

A. Who Is Speaking in the Passage (or verses)?

It may be God or the devil or a fool or even an animal! (See Numbers 22:28.) It is very important to know who is speaking.

B. To Whom Is the Word Speaking?

Is it speaking to a Christian or to a non-Christian? The meaning may be completely different because of this.

C. What Is Being Talked About in the Passage?

What came before and what comes after the passage? By answering these questions, many hard-to-understand passages can be explained.

D. When Does the Passage Speak?

In other words, during what period of history does it take place? Was it written for the time of Abraham or Moses or for the church? God talks to people in different ways at different times. It is important for Christians to follow God's teaching for today.

V. The Bible Is Holy

Because the Bible is sent from God, it should be treated with great respect. Moses told Israel, "Then the LORD spoke to you out of the fire. You heard the sound of words but saw no form; there was only a voice. He declared to you his covenant, the Ten Commandments, which he commanded you to follow and then wrote them on two stone tablets. And the LORD directed me at that time to teach you the decrees and laws you are to follow in the land that you are crossing the Jordan

34

to possess" (Deuteronomy 4:12-14).

Fill in the missing words from Revelation 22:18,19:

"I warn _____ who hears the words of the prophecy of this book: If anyone _____ anything to them, God will add to him the _____ described in this book. And if anyone _____ words away from this book of
prophecy, God will take away from him his _____ in the tree of _____
and in the holy city, which are described in this book." Both of these passages
show how serious the study of the Bible should be. God's word is holy. It should
be treated with great care.

The Bible

Fill In The Blanks:

1. What does the word "Bible" mean?

_____

_____

2. What are some names for the Bible?

    a. _____

    b. _____

    c. _____

3. The Bible was written over how many years? _____

4. How many writers did it take to write the Bible? _____

5. Name two of the prophecies that Jesus fulfilled.

    a. _____

    b. _____

6. How does the Bible help Christians? Name two blessings.

    a. _____

    b. _____

7. Give four questions to ask that help us understand the Bible.

    a. _____

    b. _____

    c. _____

    d. _____

8. In your own words, tell why we should be careful with the Bible.

    a. _____

    b. _____

9. Give the three languages that were used to write the Bible:

    a. _____

    b. _____

    c. _____

10. As an assignment, memorize the 66 books of the Bible. Say the books to a friend, tell them to your teacher or write them on a separate piece of paper.

The Church

I. What Is The Church?

A. What the Word "Church" Means

The word that Jesus chose to describe his people was an ancient Greek word, Ecclesia (ek-lay-SEE-uh), or "called out ones." The church is made up of those who have been called out of sin into holy living. They are in the world, but they no longer belong to the world. Turn to 1 Peter 2:9 and write the verse here:

_____

_____

_____

Christians have been called out of the world through the Good News. They are to do God's work now. (See 2 Corinthians 6:17,18.)

Stephen called the children of Israel in the Old Testament God's "assembly" in the wilderness (Acts 7:38). Israel had been called out of Egypt to become God's chosen people and to do his will. This was an example of what the Lord's church would be like.

B. "Church" Was Used Two Ways

In the New Testament the word "church" meant both the local group of believers and the group of believers in the whole world.

In Acts 5:11 it talks about the church in Jerusalem. Church in Acts 9:31 is used for several congregations of believers. Many times Paul spoke about groups of Christians who met in houses (see Romans 16:3-5; Colossians 4:15; Philemon 2). Paul speaks of the church as all of God's people in 1 Corinthians 10:32 and 1 Timothy 3:15. Each congregation was the church in its town. Groups of Christians may be separated by land but they are still one in Christ. They are his church.
Explain in your own words what the word "church" means:

_____

_____

II. When Did The Church Begin?

A. The Coming of the Church Is Told

The first time the word "church" is used in the New Testament is Matthew 16:18. Peter said who Jesus is—the Son of the living God. "Jesus replied, 'Blessed are you, Simon son of Jonah, for this was not revealed to you by man, but by my Father in heaven. And I tell you that you are Peter, and on this rock I will build my church, and the gates of Hades will not overcome it. I will give you the keys of the kingdom of heaven; whatever you bind on earth will be bound in heaven, and whatever you loose on earth will be loosed in heaven'" (Matthew 16:17-19). These verses seem to use the words "church" and the "kingdom of heaven" as meaning the same thing. (Turn to Colossians 1:13 and write the verse in these blanks.)

_____

_____

_____

Are members of Jesus' church also members in his kingdom? _____

The beginning of Christ's kingdom or church was mentioned before Peter's confession. John the Baptist told of the coming kingdom when he said, "Repent, for the kingdom of heaven is near" (Matthew 3:2). Jesus himself also said, "Repent, for the kingdom of heaven is near" (Matthew 4:17). In Mark 9:1, Jesus told the people, "I tell you the truth, some who are standing here will not taste death before they see the kingdom of God come with power." The kingdom was to begin with power while the apostles were living.

B. How the Church or Kingdom Began

Jesus did not start his church during his ministry on earth. According to Acts 1:6, there was going to be a special time for the start of the church. Jesus told the apostles to wait in Jerusalem until power was sent from heaven (Luke 24:49). These promises came true 50 days after Jesus rose from the dead. It was called the Day of Pentecost. (Read Acts 2:1-42 about that special day.) At that time the apostles were baptized in the Holy Spirit and received the power from heaven that Jesus promised. Peter preached the first message of the gospel (good news) and about 3,000 people believed in Jesus. They accepted Jesus as Lord, repented of their sins and were baptized into Christ (Acts 2:36-41). This was the way to get into the Lord's church. Later, Peter in Acts 11:15 said that this was the beginning of the church.

C. Prophecy Proves the Beginning of the Church

The proof for the New Testament teaching about the beginning of the church is found in the Old Testament prophets. Isaiah 2:1-3 told of how the Lord's mountain in Jerusalem would become the most important mountain. Look up these verses and fill in the missing words: "Many peoples will come and say, 'Come, let us go up to the _____ of the LORD, to the _____ of the God of Jacob. He will teach us his ways, so that we may walk in his paths.' The law will go out from _____, the word of the LORD from _____" (Isaiah 2:3).

God gave the law of Moses at Mount Sinai but he gave the good news at Mount Zion in Jerusalem. Jesus agreed with the prophecies about himself. In Luke 24:46,47 he said, "This is what is written: The Christ will suffer and rise from the dead on the third day, and repentance and forgiveness of sins will be preached in his name to all nations, beginning at Jerusalem." Jesus' church was started in Jerusalem after he rose from the dead and returned to heaven.

When was Jesus' church started? (What was the special day called?)

_____

_____

Where was the church started? _____
What part of the Old Testament talks about the starting of the church?

_____

_____

What did the people do when they heard the good news that Peter preached (Acts 2:37-39)? _____

_____

_____

III. Who Started The Church?

The church is from God. God started the church through Jesus. And, Jesus is the head of his own church.

Jesus told the apostles in Matthew 16 that it was his church. He is the builder. He is the head of the church (Colossians 1:18). Write the verse in these blanks:

_____

_____

_____

Paul called it "the church of the living God" (1 Timothy 3:15). The church is the "wife" or "bride" of Christ, which has been saved and made holy by him (Ephesians 5:25-33). The church is also called the "body of Christ" (Ephesians 1:22, 23; Colossians 1:18). The church is Christ's body, "the fullness of him who fills everything in every way" (Ephesians 1:23).

IV. How Does The Church Work?

Since the church is a kingdom, it has a King. The King has allowed the local church to choose leaders to help do his work.

A. Jesus Christ Is the Head and Lord of the Church

Fill in the missing words from these verses: Ephesians 1:22, "And God placed _____ things under his feet and appointed him _____ over everything for the _____." Ephesians 4:15, "Instead, speaking the truth in love, we will in all things grow up into _____ who is the _____, that is Christ." Ephesians 5:23, "For the husband is the _____ of the wife as _____ is the _____ of the church, his body, of which he is the _____." Colossians 1:18, "And he is the head of the _____, the church; he is the _____ and the firstborn from among the dead, so that in _____ he might have the supremacy."

1. *As the Lord of the church, Jesus has all the power!* Jesus said in Matthew 28:18, "All authority in heaven and on earth has been given to me."

2. *As the head of the church, Jesus makes all the rules!* Jesus has the power to make the rules for how his church should work. Answer the following questions from the verses below:

a. How do you become a citizen in his kingdom? (John 14:6; Mark 16:16; Acts 2:38,39)._____

_____

_____

_____

b. What do you do as a citizen in his kingdom? Tell in your own words what some of those things are (Matthew 5:3-7:27; 1 Peter 2:21).

_____

_____

_____

c. How can you be a leader in his kingdom? Give some of the main ways. (1 Timothy 3:1-13; Titus 1:5-9.) _____

_____

_____

d. What do leaders do in his kingdom? (2 Timothy 4:2; 1 Peter 5:2; Acts 6:1-6.)

_____

_____

_____

e. How are members to use money? (1 Corinthians 9:1-13; 16:1-2; 1 Timothy 5:17,18.)_____

_____

_____

f. How are citizens corrected in his kingdom? (1 Corinthians 5:1-13; 1 Thessalonians 5:14,15; 1 Timothy 5:20.) _____

_____

_____

g. How are citizens welcomed back when they fall away? (Acts 8:18-24; 2 Corinthians 2:5-11.)_____

_____

_____

Because Jesus is the head of his church, he can give the command, "Therefore go and make disciples of all nations, baptizing them in the name of the Father and of the Son and of the Holy Spirit, and teaching them to obey everything I have commanded you. And surely I am with you always, to the very end of the age" (Matthew 28:19,20).

B. Christians Choose Local Leaders

Jesus has given the church freedom to choose local leaders.

1. *How does this work?*

The choosing is up to the people in the local church. These members are the "authority" for the local work or ministry. (See Acts 6:35; 11:29,30; 1 Corinthians 16:3.)

The elders are the leaders who look out for all the people in the church. They are chosen by the church members to do this work (see 1 Peter 5:1-5). For a list of what elders do as the leaders of the church, see 1 Timothy 3:1-7 and Titus 1:5-9.

2. *What is the limit of the leader's power?*

There are limits to how much authority they have. The church has authority to make rules on things not clearly taught in the Bible. We would call these "matters of opinion." The church makes choices on daily business in order to get things done. For example, the Bible does not say how many elders or deacons (helpers) to choose. It does not say what kind of building to have. The Lord has given some choices for the local members of his kingdom to decide. The important thing is that these choices keep the believers working together!

V. What Are Some Names For The Church?

A. "Church" Is the Name Used Most

In the New Testament this is the name most often used to describe Christ's body of believers. Sometimes it is used for the place that the church meets. For example, what does Acts 9:31 say about the church?_____

_____

_____

And how does Paul address the believers in 2 Thessalonians 1:1?_____

_____

_____

_____

There was nothing else like the church when it started. There was only one church. Jesus built only one. The church was in many countries and many places but it was still called "the church." All Christians were members of this one body of believers. Turn to 1 Corinthians 1:2 and write out the verse in the blanks:

_____

_____

_____

_____

B. "Church of God" Is the Second Name Used Most

This name shows who started the church. It shows who owns the church and who planned it. It belongs to Christ and to God. (See 2 Corinthians 1:1; Galatians 1:13; 1 Timothy 3:15.)

C. The Family of God Is God's Church

1 Timothy 3:15 says, "if I am delayed, you will know how people ought to conduct themselves in God's household, which is the church of the living God, the pillar and foundation of the truth." This makes us think of the church as a family. God is the Father. Members are his sons and daughters. Romans 8:17 tells us that we will receive the blessings as God's children. How does Galatians 3:26,27 tell us we become his children?

_____

_____

_____

_____

D. The Church Is God's Temple

1 Corinthians 3:16,17 shows that we are the "temple of God." Paul says, "Don't you know that you yourselves are God's temple and that God's Spirit lives in you? If anyone destroys God's temple, God will destroy him; for God's temple is sacred, and you are that temple." The name "temple" has to do with worship. Tell in your own words what Peter says in 1 Peter 2:5:

_____

_____

_____

_____

_____

God lives in every believer by the Holy Spirit. Someday the faithful Christians will live with God forever. Revelation 21:3 gives the promise, "And I heard a loud voice from the throne saying, 'Now the dwelling of God is with men, and he will live with them. They will be his people, and God himself will be with them and be their God.'"

43

The Church

Answer True Or False:

_____ **1.** Christ's kingdom is not of this world.

_____ **2.** The "church" and the "kingdom" are two different things.

_____ **3.** Isaiah said that the kingdom would start in Galilee.

_____ **4.** The word "church" means only the local group of believers.

_____ **5.** Jesus' kingdom began on the Day of Pentecost.

_____ **6.** The church was started by John the Baptist.

_____ **7.** The word "*ecclesia*" means "called out ones."

_____ **8.** Christians are citizens of Christ's kingdom.

_____ **9.** A person can be saved but not be a member of Christ's church.

_____ **10.** The Bible says nothing about how to use money in the church.

Fill In The Blanks:

1. Galatians 3:26,27: "You are all _____ of God through faith in _____ Jesus, for all of you who were _____ in-to Christ have clothed yourselves with _____."

2. Colossians 1:18: "And he is the _____ of the body, the church; he is the _____ and the firstborn from among the dead, so that in _____ he might have the supremacy."

3. Give three names for the church:

    a. _____

    b. _____

    c. _____

Faith

I. How Is The Word "Faith" Used In The New Testament?

A. "The Faith" Is Another Name for Christianity

The word "faith" is used in place of the word "Christianity." The truth that a Christian believes is called "the faith." Jude 3 says, "Dear friends, although I was very eager to write to you about the salvation we share, I felt I had to write and urge you to contend for the faith that was once for all entrusted to the saints." Paul quotes others in Galatians 1:23, "They only heard the report: 'The man who formerly persecuted us is now preaching the faith he once tried to destroy.'" "The faith" is another way of saying Christianity.

B. Faith Is How a Christian Lives

Romans 1:17 says, "For in the gospel a righteousness from God is revealed, a righteousness that is by faith from first to last, just as it is written: 'The righteous will live by faith.'" What are some of the things that Paul thanks God for in 1 Thessalonians 1:3? _____

_____

_____

2 Corinthians 5:7 says, "We live by faith, not by sight." Christians live by faith. They also work by faith.

C. Faith Is Vital for the Non-Christian

In order to become a Christian, people who have done wrong must believe in Jesus. Like Peter, everyone must answer the question that Jesus asked him, "'But what about you?' he asked. 'Who do you say I am?' Simon Peter answered, 'You are the Christ, the Son of the living God'" (Matthew 16:15,16). Paul told the jailer at Philippi, "Believe in the Lord Jesus, and you will be saved—you and your household" (Acts 16:31; how did they obey the good news in verses 32-34?)._____

_____

45

Both Peter and Paul taught that faith in Jesus is vital. What is this kind of faith?

II. What Is Faith?

Hebrews 11:1 gives one of the best meanings for faith, "Now faith is being sure of what we hope for and certain of what we do not see." The rest of this chapter 11 gives examples of people who had faith in God. They showed their trust in God by the things they did.

Trust is another word that describes what faith really is. Faith may mean just believing the facts (a person can believe that George Washington lived but not have trust in him), but Christian faith is both believing the facts about Jesus and trusting in him as Lord and Savior. Abraham is a good example of this kind of trust, "Yet he did not waver through unbelief regarding the promise of God, but was strengthened in his faith and gave glory to God, being fully persuaded that God had power to do what he had promised" (Romans 4:20,21). Abraham trusted God completely. He believed that if he killed Isaac, God would raise him from the dead! (See Hebrews 11:17-19; turn to these verses and write them in your own words.)

_____

_____

_____

_____

III. How Do We Get Faith?

Sometimes faith seems like a big mystery. But God has given us minds to figure out mysteries. Faith is not hard to understand, even though it seems like it is.

A. Christian Faith Is Produced in a Similar Way as Other Beliefs

For example, how do we believe in the people of history? We believe that George Washington lived because of the many books written about him. There is even a statue built to honor him! Several proofs show that he lived. Or, as another example, how can we believe in our family doctor? We probably believe in him because we know others who have been treated by him. We believe that he will do a good job and can be trusted.

Faith in Christ is produced in a similar way. Christians accept several proofs in the Bible about Jesus. We believe that Jesus lived and that he is the Messiah. We believe that he is who he said he is—the Son of God. God asks us to use our common sense to see the facts about his Son. Our mind can say, "I believe in Jesus as the Christ, the Son of the living God."

B. Faith Comes From Accepting Proof

The Bible clearly says that faith comes from accepting proof about Christ. What does Jesus say in John 5:46,47?_____

_____

_____

"Jesus did many other miraculous signs in the presence of his disciples, which are not recorded in this book. But these are written that you may believe that Jesus is the Christ, the Son of God, and that by believing you may have life in his name" (John 20:30,31).

Peter said these words to the Christian brothers at the Jerusalem Council, "Brothers, you know that some time ago God made a choice among you that the Gentiles might hear from my lips the message of the gospel and believe" (Acts 15:7). Christian faith is like other beliefs—it is based on facts. Paul told the Romans how faith comes. Look up Romans 10:17 and fill in the missing words: "Consequently, faith comes from _____ the _____, and the _____ is heard through the _____ of Christ."

IV. What Does Faith Have To Do With Obedience?

Many times people do not understand what faith has to do with obedience. The Bible teaches that faith is action. Faith is obedience to what God commands.

A. How Believing Is Obeying

Paul talked about an obedient faith. Romans 1:5 says, "Through him and for his name's sake, we received grace and apostleship to call people from among all the Gentiles to the obedience that comes from faith." (See Romans 16:26 also.) Write Acts 6:7 in the blanks:_____

_____

_____

_____

Believing is obeying. Obedience comes from true faith in Jesus.

There are two kinds of obedience. One is obedience because of faith in God. The other is because of wanting to please other people. The first kind of obedience comes from God. The second kind comes from man. Sometimes a person will be honest only because it is "good for business." He only wants to please men. He may not really want to please God.

God wants to know if we obey him out of love and faith or for some other reason. All through history God has asked man to show his faith by obedience. For example, in the Garden of Eden, there was no obvious reason for Eve not to eat of the fruit of the tree. But God told Adam and Eve not to do it. When Eve chose to eat the fruit, she disobeyed God. God had simply told them not to eat of the tree in the middle of the garden. Adam and Eve did what they wanted to do anyway!

God asks us to be obedient and to show our faith in what he commands. One of these "tests" of our faith is Christian baptism. There is no clear or obvious way to explain that baptism is part of becoming a Christian. God simply commands us to be baptized! In Mark 16:16, Jesus told his followers, "Whoever believes and is baptized will be saved, but whoever does not believe will be condemned." Peter told people on the Day of Pentecost, "Repent and be baptized, every one of you, in the name of Jesus Christ for the forgiveness of your sins. And you will receive the gift of the Holy Spirit. The promise is for you and your children and for all who are far off—for all whom the Lord our God will call" (Acts 2:38,39). When a person is baptized, he does it because Jesus commanded it. This shows faith in what Jesus said. It is also a "test" of our love for Christ. Write John 14:15 on these blanks:

_____

_____

_____

_____

B. How Obeying Is Faith in Action

This is what James was talking about when he said that faith without action is no faith at all. Remember, even the demons believe that there is one God. (See James 2:14-26.) Abraham proved his faith when he offered his son Isaac as a sacrifice. He obeyed God when his faith did all the action. You really do not have true faith until you are obedient to God. This settles any question about being saved by faith only or by obedience only. Faith and obedience together save! They cannot be separated.

V. What Are Some Blessings Of Faith?

Here are some reasons that make faith so important to Christians:

A. Faith Is How to Receive All of God's Blessings

God has always saved and blessed people because of their faith. Ephesians 2:8 says, "For it is by grace you have been saved, through faith—and this not from yourselves, it is the gift of God. . . ." It is because of God's love and mercy that we have these blessings. Faith is the key to receiving these blessings.

B. Faith Has Special Blessings

Faith saves people. Peter said these words about the non-Jews (Gentiles), "He made no distinction between us and them, for he purified their hearts by faith" (Acts 15:9). Faith is the way that we accept God's gift of salvation. Peter also said, "All the prophets testify about him that everyone who believes in him receives forgiveness of sins through his name" (Acts 10:43). When the Bible talks about being saved by faith, it means an obedient faith. This is what Peter meant by 1 Peter 1:22, "Now that you have purified yourselves by obeying the truth so that you have sincere love for your brothers, love one another deeply, from the heart." What did Paul say about obeying in Romans 6:16?

_____

_____

_____

_____

One of worst ways to hurt God is for a person not to believe his Word. But faith makes God happy! Look up Hebrews 11:6 and fill in the missing words: "And without _____ it is _____ to please God, because anyone who comes to him must _____ that he exists and that he _____ those who earnestly seek him." Faith can bring peace to your heart. Just before Jesus went back to heaven, he told his apostles, "Do not let your hearts be troubled. Trust God; trust also in me" (John 14:1). The apostles would find comfort for their sad hearts because they believed in Jesus. Turn to Matthew 6:25-34 and list the ways that our heavenly Father takes care of us:

_____

_____

_____

_____

Faith

Answer True Or False:

_____ **1.** Demons do not believe that there is one God.

_____ **2.** Having faith is good, but you really don't need it.

_____ **3.** "Trust" is another word for faith.

_____ **4.** Obedience has nothing to do with faith in Jesus.

Answer The Following:

1. What is another way that the word "faith" is used?

2. Based on what you have learned in this lesson, how would you explain what faith is?

_____
_____
_____
_____

3. Give some blessings of faith.

    a. _____

    b. _____

    c. _____

4. Choose one of the people in Hebrews 11 and tell why (and how) you think that person proved his or her faith in God.

_____
_____
_____

Repentance

One of the very first to ask people to repent was Noah. 2 Peter 2:5 says that Noah was "a preacher of righteousness." Being right with God is what "repentance" is all about. Noah tried to save the people of his day from the flood. He tried to get the people to change their hearts and lives. Turn in your Bible to Joel 2:12,13 and fill in the missing words: "'Even now,' declares the LORD, 'return to me with all your _____, with fasting and weeping and mourning.' Rend your _____ and not your garments. _____ to the LORD your God, for he is gracious and compassionate, slow to anger and abounding in _____, and he relents from sending calamity." The first prophet in the New Testament, John the Baptist came preaching in the desert of Judea. Fill in the blanks from Matthew 3:2: "_____, for the kingdom of _____ is near." What did Jesus say to the people when he started preaching? (Find your answer in Mark 1:15.)

_____

_____

_____

When the church was started, the message was the same. Peter told the people on the Day of Pentecost to "Repent and be baptized, every one of you, in the name of Jesus Christ for the forgiveness of your sins. And you will receive the gift of the Holy Spirit" (Acts 2:38). Jesus' message did not change all through the New Testament. The last book, Revelation, tells about the letters to the seven churches. Jesus told them to change their hearts and lives. People today need to hear the same message! Let's find out what "repentance" means.

I. What Is Repentance?

A. What Repentance Means

The New Testament was first written in the Greek language. The word that was first used for "repentance" was a word that meant to "have another mind" or to "change the mind." When you "repent," you are changing your mind about sin. It means to turn away from sin. Repentance has three parts:

1. We change our mind (or what we want to do).
2. We change because we feel sorry for our sins.
3. We change how we act and live.

B. How to Picture Repentance

Turn to 2 Corinthians 7:9 and fill in the missing words: "yet now I am happy, not because you were made _____, but because your _____ led you to repentance. For you became _____ as God intended and so were not harmed in any way by us." In the very next verse, what does Paul say about this kind of feeling sorry?

_____

_____

Luke 15 is another way to picture repentance. Luke wrote the story Jesus told about a special young son. This son refused to stay with his father and ran away. He went to another country far away. Tell in your own words what happened to him (Luke 15:14-16):

_____

_____

_____

What did the son realize? (Luke 15:17)

_____

_____

_____

What did he decide to do after he was sorry for his sin? (Luke 15:18,19)

_____

_____

_____

_____

So, the young son changed his mind, was sorry for his sin, then what is the last part of repenting? Instead of sitting in the pig pen, what happened? Luke 15:20 says, "So he got up and went to his father." He changed what he did and how he lived. Do you see the picture of repentance? The young son changed his heart and mind. This caused him to change the way he lived!

Just being sorry for sin is not repentance. Anyone can be sorry that he got caught. What is important is that a person be sorry for the wrong things he does enough to change his actions. Being afraid of judgment is not repentance. A person can be afraid of what God will do to him, but when things get better, he forgets all about

52

changing his life. Turn to Acts 24:25,26 and tell in your own words what Felix did: _____

_____

_____

_____

II. How Are People Led To Repentance?

The Bible teaches that there are reasons that make people want to repent.

Let's look at three of them.

A. People Are Led by the Love of God

Write the reason that Paul gives in Romans 2:4 for people to change their hearts and minds: _____

_____

_____

_____

Fill in the blanks from 1 John 4:19: "We _____ because he first _____ us." This is the greatest reason that causes us to change. When we see God's love in giving Jesus on the cross, we want to change our heart and life.

B. People Are Led by Feeling Sorry for Sin

Turn to 2 Corinthians 7:10 and answer the following question. What leads to salvation?

_____

_____

_____

When you know what sin does to God, to your family and to your friends—you are truly sorry. Being sorry for sin leads to changing your heart and life or "repentance."

There are two kinds of being sorry. One is being sad the way God wants. The other is the way the world wants you to be sad. Judas is an example of the way the world wants us to be sorry. He turned Jesus in to the Romans to crucify him. He was sorry after he did it. But, he did not change his heart and life! Peter is an example of being sad the way that God wants. Jesus was able to use Peter because he was sorry for his sin.

C. People Are Led by the Fear of Judgment

What did Paul tell the people of Athens? Turn to Acts 17:30,31 and tell why people should change.

_____
_____
_____
_____

This may not be the best reason to repent, but it may be the only reason for some people. It is likely for most people that God uses all three reasons to bring people to change.

III. What Does Making Things Right Have To Do With Repentance?

The Bible teaches that a person should try to make things right again when he has repented. He should try to correct the wrong things that were done, as much as possible.

John the Baptist said, "Produce fruit in keeping with repentance" (Matthew 3:8). Remember Zacchaeus? Turn to Luke 19:8,9 and write in your own words what Zacchaeus did when he changed his heart and life.

_____
_____
_____
_____

In your own life is there something that you have done wrong that you need to make right? Write some ways that would help correct the situation.

_____
_____
_____

IV. Why Do We Have To Repent?

One of the reasons that we need to repent is because Jesus told us to repent. Just before he went back to heaven, he told his followers in Luke 24:46-48: "This is what is written: The Christ will suffer and rise from the dead on the third day, and repentance and forgiveness of sins will be preached in his name to all nations, beginning at Jerusalem. You are witnesses of these things." Read Luke 13:1-5, then write verse 3 in the space:

_____

_____

_____

Paul told the people of Athens to repent. Fill in the missing words from Acts 17:30: "In the past God _____ such ignorance, but now he _____ all people everywhere to _____." Turn to 2 Peter 3:9 and answer the question: God wants whose heart and life changed?

_____

A. Repentance—What Non-Christians Must Do

The reason for preaching the Good News is that people will be saved from their sins. A person must have his heart pure from sin. (Peter told the people on the Day of Pentecost how this could happen. Read Acts 2:38,39 again to see what he told them.) Turn to 1 Peter 1:22 and tell how a person is made pure:_____

_____

_____

_____

B. Repentance—What Christians Must Do

What does a Christian do to be forgiven of sin? John wrote to Christians about this. Turn to 1 John 2:1,2 and fill in the missing words: "My dear children, I write this to you so that you will not _____. But if anybody does _____, we have one who speaks to the Father in our _____—Jesus Christ, the Righteous One. He is the atoning _____ for our sins, and not only for ours but also for the sins of the _____ world." (Also see Acts 8:22 for another example.) Christians are to pray for forgiveness and then change their hearts and lives.

V. What Stops People From Repenting?

A. Pride Stops People From Repenting

Turn to Acts 7:51 and write in the blanks why the Jewish leaders did not repent:_____

_____

_____

Everybody has some pride. It is hard to say that we have sin. Pride makes us want to keep doing wrong things. Pride makes it hard to say that we are weak. Jesus said that you must become like "what" to enter the kingdom of heaven? (Find your answer in Matthew 18:3) _____. The lost son had to do this very thing in Luke 15 to be able to go back to his father.

B. Putting Things Off Stops People From Repenting

Many people are in the habit of putting things off to do later. Some go to the end of their life without changing their heart and life. Like Felix in Acts 25:24-27, they look for a better time to repent. The Bible tries to tell us that today is the time to be saved. Heaven is too wonderful, hell is too awful and time is too short to put off changing our hearts and lives. There will not be a better time to repent!

Repentance

Answer The Following:

1. How would you explain what repentance is?

_____

_____

_____

_____

2. What are two things that stop people from repenting?

a. _____

b. _____

3. Paul talks about two kinds of being sorry in 2 Corinthians 7:7-11. What are they?

a. _____

b. _____

Answer True or False:

_____ **1.** Making things right is part of repentance.

_____ **2.** The love of God is the only reason for repenting.

_____ **3.** You must become like a child to get into heaven.

_____ **4.** God does not want anybody to be lost.

_____ **5.** Jesus never told people to repent.

Baptism

Jesus said in Matthew 16:26, "What good will it be for a man if he gains the whole world, yet forfeits his soul? Or what can a man give in exchange for his soul?" Any subject that has to do with saving your soul is important. Turn to Mark 16:16 and write the verse in the blanks:

_____

_____

_____

Jesus thought being baptized was important. He walked almost 70 miles from Nazareth to the Jordan River to be baptized by John as an example for us. Baptism is clearly part of the eight examples of people being saved in the book of Acts. Jesus and his apostles believed that baptism was part of obedience. Therefore, we must think of it as important too.

This lesson will study what the New Testament teaches about baptism. We will answer these questions: 1) Who told us to be baptized? 2) How are we to be baptized? 3) Who is to be baptized? and, 4) Why are we to be baptized?

I. Who Told Us To Be Baptized?

Turn in your Bible to Matthew 28:18-20 and fill in the missing words: "Then Jesus came to them and said, 'All _____ in heaven and on earth has been given to me. Therefore go and make _____ of all nations, _____ them in the name of the Father and of the Son and of the Holy Spirit, and _____ them to obey _____ I have commanded you. And surely I am with you always, to the very end of the age.'" According to these verses, who told us to be baptized? _____

Peter told people on the Day of Pentecost to be baptized. Turn to Acts 2:38 and answer the question: In whose name are we told to be baptized? _____ _____ When we are told to do this in Jesus' name—what do you think it means? _____

_____

_____

59

II. How Should We Be Baptized?

A. What the Bible Says

The Bible was written so that everyone could understand it. God also wants everyone to be saved. So, the things that we need to do to be saved are written clearly. Look up each of the following verses to see how a person is to be baptized.

1. *What is needed for a person to be baptized?*
(Turn to Acts 10:46,47 to answer this question.)_____
_____ (See Matthew 3:13 also.)

2. *Does it take a lot of what is needed for a person to be baptized?* (Turn to John 3:23 to find your answer.)_____
_____

3. *What does a person do in baptism?* (Turn to Acts 8:38,39 to answer this question.)_____
_____
_____

(Also turn to Mark 1:10 to find help for your answer.)

How does the New Testament say a person is to be baptized? It takes water, going into the water with the one doing the baptizing, and coming up out of the water. (You will see that Acts 8:26-40 is a good example of this.) The Bible teaches that being immersed (dunked under water) is Christian baptism.

B. What Baptism Pictures

Many times God gives a spiritual meaning for something that is done. Baptism is not just something that is done. There is a spiritual meaning attached to it.

1. *Baptism is a picture of dying and coming to life again.*

Turn to Romans 6:1-5 to see this picture. Fill in the missing words from these verses: "What shall we say, then? Shall we go on sinning so that _____ may increase? By no means! We _____to sin; how can we live in it any longer? Or don't you know that all of us who were _____ into Christ Jesus were _____ into his death? We were therefore _____ with him through baptism into death in order that, just as Christ was raised from the dead through the glory of the Father, we too may live a new life. If we have been _____ with him like this in his death, we will certainly also be united with him in his _____.” This is a picture of the good news that Jesus came to bring. Jesus' death, burial and rising from the dead are pictured in baptism. Every time a person is baptized we should see this picture. Baptism tells us that Jesus loved us enough to give his life for us.

Baptism is also a picture of dying to our old sinful lives. The old life is crucified and buried in water. By faith and repentance (changing our hearts and lives) a person joins with Christ. We are baptized into Christ. We are buried with him so that we could live a new life! Only being immersed clearly pictures all of these things.

2. *Baptism is a picture of being born.*

The first time the idea of being "born again" is seen in the New Testament is John 3:5. Turn to this verse and write it in the blanks:

_____

_____

_____

Turn to 2 Corinthians 5:17. What does a Christian become?

_____

_____

This is what Paul was talking about in Romans 6:1-5. Baptism clearly gives this picture of being born again! Fill in the missing words from Titus 3:5: "He _____ us, not because of righteous things we had done, but because of his mercy. He _____ us through the _____ of rebirth and renewal by the Holy Spirit."

C. What Baptism Means

The New Testament was written in the Greek language. Baptism comes from the Greek word *baptizo* (bap-tee-zo) which means "to dip, immerse, or dunk." Jesus could have used other Greek words that meant other things. He did not. He used the word *baptizo* or baptize by immersing. From what we learn in the New Testament, we can say that baptism is being immersed or dunked in water.

III. Who Is To Be Baptized?

Not everybody is ready to be baptized. What kind of person should be baptized? Think about these two things:

A. A Person Should Be a Believer in Christ

We know this from Mark 16:16. What does it say again?

_____

_____

What did the Corinthians do in Acts 18:8?

_____

_____

B. A Person Should Be Sorry for His Sins

Remember what Romans 6:1-5 says about dying to the old sinful life? That is why Peter told the people in Acts 2:38,39 to "Repent and be baptized, every one of you, in the name of Jesus Christ for the forgiveness of your sins"—they needed to be sorry for their sins. A person must "die to sin" before he can be buried with Christ in baptism.

IV. Why Should We Be Baptized?

Since Jesus is the One who told us to be baptized, he is the One to tell us why. Jesus and his apostles give us several reasons:

A. In Order to Be Saved

Mark 16:16 tells us what Jesus said. Turn to 1 Peter 3:21 and put the verse in your own words:_____

_____

_____

B. For the Forgiveness of Sins

What did Peter tell the people on the Day of Pentecost (Acts 2:38,39)?_____

_____

_____

_____

C. For Washing Away Sin

Turn to Acts 22:16 and write the verse in the blanks:_____

_____

_____
_____

This was part of what Paul was to be told to do by Ananias (see verse 22:10). Jesus had told Paul, "Now get up and go into the city, and you will be told what you must do" (Acts 9:6).

D. To Become Part of Christ

What did Paul tell the Romans in chapter 6:3?_____
_____
_____
_____

Into Whom are we baptized? (Turn to Galatians 3:26,27 and Acts 19:1-5 for your answer.) _____
_____
_____
_____

Turn to the following verses and tell the blessings of being "in Christ":
Romans 3:24:_____
_____
Romans 8:1:_____
_____
Philippians 2:1: _____
_____
1 Corinthians 15:22: _____
_____
2 Corinthians 5:17:_____
_____
Colossians 2:9-12:_____
_____

Because all of these blessings are for those "in Christ," do you see the importance of being baptized "into Christ?" Is it clear that baptism is part of salvation? Baptism alone will not save a person. The New Testament teaches that when a person believes in Christ and is truly sorry for his sins, he is to be baptized for the forgiveness of his sins.

Baptism

Match the Quote With The Verses:

_____ **1.** "Repent and be baptized, every one of you, in the name of Jesus Christ for the forgiveness of your sins."

_____ **2.** "As soon as Jesus was baptized, he went up out of the water."

_____ **3.** "Whoever believes and is baptized will be saved."

_____ **4.** "We were therefore buried with him through baptism into death."

_____ **5.** "This water symbolizes baptism that now saves you also."

_____ **6.** "When they came up out of the water, the Spirit of the Lord suddenly took Philip away."

_____ **7.** "And many of the Corinthians believed and were baptized."

_____ **8.** "And now what are you waiting for? Get up, be baptized and wash your sins away, calling on his name."

_____ **9.** "Therefore go and make disciples of all nations, baptizing them in the name of the Father and of the Son and of the Holy Spirit."

a. 1 Peter 3:21	d. Acts 2:38	g. Acts 8:39
b. Mark 16:16	e. Romans 6:4	h. Acts 22:16
c. Matthew 28:19	f. Matthew 3:16	i. Acts 18:8

Answer These Questions:

1. Baptism is a picture of what? _____

_____

2. What does the Greek word *baptizo* mean? _____

_____

3. What are some blessings of being "in Christ?"

a. _____

b. _____

c. _____

d. _____

The Lord's Supper

Men have built many statues or monuments to remember other people. In Washington, D.C., the Washington Monument reaches high into the sky, in memory of the first President of the United States. The Lincoln Memorial also stands in honor of President Lincoln. In Arlington Cemetery, the tomb of the Unknown Soldier was built to honor soldiers who gave their lives for their country.

In time, all memorials built by men will fall apart. But when Jesus gave us his memorial, he gave one that will last as long as the earth does. His memorial is called the "Lord's Supper."

Men like to use rare and expensive materials to build memorials. Jesus chose common materials. He chose bread and grape juice. Wheat for making bread and grapes for the juice can be found in almost every part of the world. Therefore, Jesus' memorial can be shared around the world.

Men build memorials out of materials that will last a long time. Jesus chose materials that are very weak and do not last a long time. Bread can get moldy. Grape juice can spoil. Jesus did not mean for his memorial to last because of the materials. He wanted his memorial to last because of the love of God in the hearts of his people.

I. When Was The Lord's Supper First Celebrated?

A. How Did it Begin?

Jesus chose to celebrate the Lord's Supper during the Passover Feast of the Jews. Turn to Luke 22:15,16. How much did Jesus want to eat the last Passover with his followers? _____ During the Jewish Passover meal, there were four cups of wine (watered grape juice) that they drank in a special order. It was probably after the third cup that Jesus gave the Lord's Supper.

Jesus' new memorial was simple compared with the Jewish way of having the Passover meal. Write Luke 22:19 in the space:_____

_____

_____

Why was Jesus' blood poured out? (Find your answer in Matthew 26:28.)_____

_____

_____

B. What Materials Were Used?

1. *The bread*

Jesus used the bread without yeast from the Passover meal. Read Deuteronomy 16:1-8. For how many days were the Jews to eat the bread without yeast?_____

_____

Why were they to eat this meal? _____

When were they to eat the Passover meal? _____

In Matthew 26:26, for what does Jesus say the bread stands?_____

_____

_____

2. *The fruit of the vine*

The second part of the Lord's Supper is called the "cup" or the "fruit of the vine." These words mean grape juice. Read Matthew 26:26-30. What does Jesus say the cup or grape juice pictures?_____

_____

_____

_____

II. What Are Some Names For The Lord's Supper?

A. To Break Bread

In the New Testament, the Lord's Supper is most often called "the breaking of bread." Turn to Acts 2:40-42. Why did the early Christians meet?_____

_____

In Acts 20:7, why did the Christians meet at Troas? _____

_____

66

On which day of the week? _____ In 1 Corinthians 10:16,17, how does Paul describe the Lord's Supper? _____

_____

_____

The followers of Jesus probably knew what the "breaking of bread" meant when Jesus was taken down from the cross. The first time that they shared the memorial supper they could picture how Jesus' body was broken on the cross. That is what we should see each time we eat the bread—in memory of Jesus' broken body.

B. The Lord's Table

The table belongs to the Lord. Look up 1 Corinthians 10:21. Fill in the missing words: "You cannot drink the cup of the _____ and the cup of demons too; you cannot have a part in both the _____ table and the table of demons." Jesus is the one who gave the supper in the first place. He is the host at every meal. Read Matthew 18:20. What did Jesus promise his followers?_____

_____

_____

This is true whenever the church meets. It is especially true when the church meets at the Lord's table.

C. The Lord's Supper

The Lord's Supper is perhaps the most used name for the meal today. It is called the Lord's Supper because the Lord gave it. He invites his children to come and eat. He is the one who is hurt when a Christian does not want to come to the meal. Jesus is the source of spiritual food. How does Christ want us to eat? Turn to Luke 22:19 and write what Jesus said in the blanks: _____

_____

_____

Only Jesus can be the one to turn a child of God away from the table. It is the Lord's table. The word "supper" is probably used because of the example of the meal in Matthew 26:20 (see parallels) and Acts 20:7. Since it was an evening meal, the word "supper" is used.

D. Time of Sharing or Communion

The name "communion" is often used today for the Lord's Supper. This word is used more to describe what is happening. Turn to 1 Corinthians 10:16. How does

Paul explain what we do in the Lord's Supper? _____

_____

_____

_____

III. When Do We Share The Lord's Supper?

When Jesus gave the Lord's Supper he did not tell us the time or how often to have it. Jesus left many things for the Holy Spirit to teach the apostles (see John 16:12,13). He simply said to eat the Lord's Supper "to remember me." When the church was started on the Day of Pentecost, the apostles were careful to do what Jesus said. Acts 2:42 further explains this. Fill in the missing words from this verse: "They devoted themselves to the apostles' teaching and to _____, to the _____ of bread and to _____." They may have been worshiping God much of the time! Some think that they even had the Lord's Supper every day for a while. (Acts 2:46 is a possible example of this.)

The first clear proof of how often the early Christians shared the Lord's Supper is Acts 20:7. What does that verse say about the day and how often they ate the supper? _____

_____

There are some other reasons to believe that the early Christians shared the Lord's Supper every week. Here are some of the reasons:

A. New Testament Examples

The meeting at Troas in Acts 20 was a meeting for a reason. They were meeting to "break bread" together. It sounds like a custom or habit that they were meeting on the first day of the week. So we have an example of weekly worship. Even though they heard Paul speak, the main reason for meeting was to share in the breaking of bread or "communion."

Paul also wrote to the Corinthians about the Lord's Supper. Read 1 Corinthians 11:17-34. This long passage was written by Paul to correct some problems over the Lord's Supper. What did Paul say about their meetings? (verse 11:17) _____

_____

_____

From whom had Paul received his teaching about the Lord's Supper? (11:23)

_____

68

What did Paul say that the Corinthians would show each time they ate this Supper? (11:26) _____

_____

_____

The Corinthians were not behaving well at the Lord's Table. They were misusing the main purpose of the Lord's Supper—for unity of the believers.
Tell in your own words how they were not obeying the Lord.

_____

_____

_____

B. Old Testament Examples

When God told Moses how to build the Tabernacle, he was doing more than just giving him a tent for worshiping in the desert. The Tabernacle was to prepare Israel for the coming of the Christ. The Tabernacle courtyard was probably a picture of the world. The Holy Place was an example of the church today. The Most Holy Place (Holy of Holies) was an example of heaven.

In the Holy Place (an example of the church today) there were three pieces of furniture:

1. *The gold lampstand* gave light for the room. This was a picture of God's word. The word gives light and helps guide our steps. Turn to Psalm 119:105 and write the verse in the blanks: _____

_____

2. *The altar for burning incense* represented the prayers of those who believed in God. (See Exodus 37:25-29 and Exodus 40:26,27 for more on this piece of furniture.) Turn to Revelation 5:8 and write the verse in the blanks: _____

_____

_____

_____

3. *The table* was used for the twelve loaves of bread each week. The priests were told to set the loaves in place each week and to leave the loaves on the table for one week. The priests would eat the old bread when they brought in the new loaves. This was in worship of Jehovah. The bread was to remind the people of Israel of the presence and special care of God. The Lord's Supper should remind us of Jesus' presence. The bread and the grape juice should cause us to remember that God's blessings come through Jesus. The fact that the priests ate the bread faithfully each week is an example that the Lord's Supper may have been intended to be weekly also.

C. Teaching of the Church Fathers

The name "Church Fathers" means the leaders of the early church. These were the ones who led especially right after the apostles died. The writings of these men were not Scripture, but they do show how the church worshiped after the time of the apostles.

One of these men was Justin Martyr. He wrote about 125 years after Christ. He was a follower of Polycarp who was a follower of the apostle John. This means that his teaching on the Lord's Supper is very close to the teachings of the apostles. He told how they met on Sunday and shared the Lord's Supper. Other Church Fathers tell that the church practiced the same thing for 200 years in the western part of the church and for 700 years in the Greek Church.

IV. What Is The Meaning Of The Lord's Supper?

A. To Remember Christ's Death

The Lord's Supper is a weekly table of remembering. A memorial should help with three things:

1. It satisfies the desire of your heart to do some loving thing for the Lord. The Lord's Supper lets us do that. What did Jesus say in 1 Corinthians 11:24? (Turn to this verse and write your answer.)_____

_____

_____

2. By observing this meal often we are less likely to forget what Christ has done.

3. By its symbols of bread and grape juice, it reminds us of the very important fact of the good news in 1 Corinthians 15:3. Write this verse in the blanks:

_____

_____

_____

70

B. To Preach the Good News

Each Lord's Day every believer is preaching a sermon!

1. *We preach the Lord's death.*
What does 1 Corinthians 11:26 say?_____
_____
_____

What does Jesus say about the cup? (Look up Luke 22:20.)_____
_____
_____
_____

The Lord's Supper is a monument to our salvation and to Christ himself. The Lord's Supper teaches that man is bought and receives forgiveness of sins through the blood of Jesus. (See Ephesians 1:7 and 1 Peter 1:18-20; write what these verses mean in your own words):_____
_____
_____
_____

2. *We preach our love for him.*

When the Christian meets at the table, he is telling the Lord and the world that he believes that Jesus' blood has bought him. He is also being obedient to his Lord's command. Christ's love caused him to die for man. (See Romans 5:6-8.) The same love brings Christians to love Christ and to be present at his table.

3. *We preach the Lord's return.*

Paul says that when we eat the Lord's Supper, we "Proclaim the Lord's death until he comes" (1 Corinthians 11:26). The Lord's table looks back to the cross where our salvation was made possible. It looks to the future to the day when Christ will return and our salvation will be fully complete. Believers of all time will be gathered together to be with the Lord who has bought them and saved them from sin. Only those who truly look forward to his second coming will want to be at the Lord's Supper as often as possible.

The Lord's Supper

Matching

Read all four of these accounts of the Lord's Supper and then match the verses with the quotes—Matthew 26:26-30; Mark 14:22-25; Luke 22:19,20; 1 Corinthians 11:23-28:

_____ **1.** "This is my blood of the covenant, which is poured out for many."

_____ **2.** "When they had sung a hymn, they went out to the Mount of Olives."

_____ **3.** "For whenever you eat this bread and drink this cup, you proclaim the Lord's death until he comes."

_____ **4.** "And he took bread, gave thanks and broke it, and gave it to them, saying 'This is my body given for you; do this in remembrance of me.'"

_____ **5.** "A man ought to examine himself before he eats of the bread and drinks of the cup."

Answer The Following Questions:

1. What are three other names for the Lord's Supper?

a._____

b._____

c._____

2. What are four reasons for having the Lord's Supper every week?

a._____

b._____

c._____

d._____

3. How can you preach the good news by eating the Lord's Supper? Name three ways.

a._____

b._____

c._____

Prayer

I. When Did Prayer Begin?

Other than the conversations between God and man in Genesis 2 and 3, the first mention of "prayer" in the Bible is in Genesis 4:26. Turn to that verse in your Bible and write it in the blanks: _____

_____

The Bible does not say that God commanded men to pray at that time. Prayer seems to have begun out of man's free will. Man felt his need for God and began to call upon him. Prayer to God should be as natural as a child talking to his father or mother. When man truly knows and understands God, he will want to talk to him.

II. What Is Prayer?

A. Prayer Is Asking God for Something

Asking for God's blessings is at the heart of prayer. Prayer always springs out of a need, either for yourself or for someone else. Turn in your Bible to Hebrews 11:6. What does it say that a person must believe? _____

_____

Jesus told his followers to do something in Matthew 7:7. What did he tell them to do? _____

_____

Even though God knows our needs before we ask, he still is glad to have his children come to him with our desires. He finds joy in giving the things we need.

B. Prayer Is Thanking God for Something

A second important part of prayer is giving thanks and praising God. Our asking God makes known our needs. Our thanking God shows our gratitude. What did Paul tell the Philippians in chapter 4, verse 6? Write the verse here:_____

73

_____

_____

In your own words, tell what Paul told Timothy in 1 Timothy 2:1: _____

_____

_____

Thanksgiving and praise to God show gratitude for blessings that God has given in the past. This is pleasing to God. God deserves to be thanked! It also makes us ready to receive God's answer to our prayers. What did Paul tell the Christians at Thessalonica? Write 1 Thessalonians 5:18 here: _____

_____

_____

III. How Can Prayer Be Effective?

God's promises sometimes have "conditions." This is true with prayer. He has promised to answer our prayers. But he has also given certain conditions which we must meet before God will answer our prayers. Here are a few of those conditions.

A. Pray With Pure Hearts and Clean Hands

Turn to Psalm 66:18. When does the Lord not hear a prayer? _____

_____

Paul told Timothy about prayer in 1 Timothy 2:8. Write the verse in the blanks:

_____

_____

God is a holy God. There is no sin in him and he will not put up with sin in those who come into his presence through prayer. These verses refer to sin in the lives of his children. When he says he will not hear, he may not answer in the way that is expected. This does not include the prayer for forgiveness. Prayer out of a heart that turns from sin is the kind God wants to hear. God has promised to answer that prayer (1 John 1:9 and Acts 8:22). God does not hear the prayer of a Christian who asks for some blessing but does not want to repent of sin in his life.

God told Israel in Isaiah 59:1,2, "Surely the arm of the LORD is not too short to save, nor his ear too dull to hear. But your iniquities have separated you from your God; your sins have hidden his face from you, so that he will not hear." One of

74

the best ways that God will hear our prayers is to begin them by truly asking forgiveness. This is always pleasing to him.

B. Pray After Hearing and Doing God's Will

How does John tell us to receive what we ask? (Turn to 1 John 3:22 for your answer.) _____

_____

A second condition that helps prayer to be effective is keeping God's commandments. What does Proverbs 28:9 say about refusing to obey? _____

_____

God is not foolish. He will not keep pouring his blessings on a willful and disobedient child. Nothing pleases a parent more than to give to an obedient child. God feels the same way. Are you honestly trying to do God's will before asking for his blessings and gifts? The blind man in John 9:31 had something to say about this. Write the verse in the blanks: _____

_____

C. Pray in God's Will

Jesus showed this teaching in the Garden of Gethsemane. How did Jesus pray in Matthew 26:39? Whose will should always be first in our prayers? _____

_____

Turn to 1 John 5:14. When does God hear our prayers? _____

_____

Our heavenly Father who is all wise knows what is best for his kingdom—and what is best for us. The apostle Paul said, "In the same way, the Spirit helps us in our weakness. We do not know what we ought to pray for, but the Spirit himself intercedes for us with groans that words cannot express" (Romans 8:26). We do not always know what God's will is. We should ask for blessings if it is his will and best for the kingdom. Another reason to pray that his will is done is because we do not know what is best for us. Like a wise parent, God does not always give us what we ask. We should leave it up to God to decide what blessings we need or do not need.

D. Pray Sincerely and Be Persistent (Stay with it)

How does James tell us to pray in James 5:16? _____

James explains what he meant in verse 17 by reminding us of Elijah. He first prayed that God would not send the rain. So God stopped the rain for three years and six months! Then he earnestly prayed to God and God sent the rain again. God hears this kind of prayer according to his will and because we are sincere. God does not like half-hearted prayers. A true, heart-felt prayer pleases God.

Along with honesty, we must "stay with it" when we pray. What does Paul say in 1 Thessalonians 5:17? _____

_____

This means that we should always be ready to pray. Fill in the missing words from Ephesians 6:18: "And pray in the _____ on all occasions with all _____ of prayers and requests. With this in mind, be _____ and always keep on praying for all the _____." Even Jesus told his followers in Luke 18:1, "that they should always pray and not give up."

E. Pray for Others

Another condition for prayer to be effective is that we must pray for others. Why is it that James says we do not receive things from God? (James 4:3) _____

_____

_____

We should always put God's kingdom and his will first. It is easy to think of God as a Santa Claus. We think that we can ask him for everything. This picture of God is not true. God will answer according to his will. Often we would be hurt if God gave us everything that we asked. He chooses the things that we need and will help us grow to be like Jesus.

F. Pray in the Name of Christ

Another condition for effective prayer is to pray to the Father in the name of Christ. This is what Jesus told his followers in John 14:13,14: "And I will do whatever you ask in my name, so that the Son may bring glory to the Father. You may ask me for anything in my name, and I will do it." Write John 16:24 in the blanks:

_____

_____

Here are a few reasons that Christians should pray in the name of Christ:

1. *Jesus made it possible for us to go to the Father.*

Turn to Hebrews 10:19,20 and write in your own words what these verses mean:

_____

_____

Hebrews chapter 9 teaches that a new way was opened by Jesus to the Father. Because of Jesus' death and resurrection from the dead, there is a new and direct line to God. We may enter God's presence through prayer!

2. *Jesus is our go-between.*

Paul told Timothy in 1 Timothy 2:5, "For there is one God and one mediator between God and men, the man Christ Jesus." Through Jesus we can reach heaven. Through Jesus we can receive heaven's blessings from God. Christ is a two-way connection between earth and heaven.

3. *Christ is standing at the throne of God.*

What does Paul say that Jesus is doing now? (Romans 8:34) _____

_____

Our name would mean almost nothing at the throne of God if we did not belong to Christ. Christ is above every creature in the universe (Philippians 2:9). Therefore, when we come to God in the name of Christ, we are coming in the greatest name in heaven and earth. We can come to the throne of God through him (Hebrews 4:14-16).

4. *Our sins have been washed away in the blood of Christ.*

It means that we have been cleansed and made worthy by him to stand in God's presence (Revelation 1:5 and Hebrews 9:14). Because of these and other reasons, our prayers to God should always be given in the name of and by the authority of Jesus Christ, our high priest, go-between, Savior, and Lord.

G. Pray in Faith

How does Jesus say to pray in Mark 11:24? _____

_____

Fill in the blanks from James 1:6-8: "But when he asks, he must _____ and not _____, because he who _____ is like a wave of the sea, blown and tossed by the wind."

What does Hebrews 11:6 say about faith?_____
_____

We can pray in faith because we are coming to God who is all-powerful and who can answer the prayers of his children. The Christian can pray in faith knowing he is coming to one who loves him and desires to answer what he asks. The Christian has every reason to pray believing that his prayers will be answered.

We must always keep in mind that God's will and wisdom will decide God's answer. This does not stop us from praying in faith, believing that God will answer our prayer. Even when God in his wisdom says no to what we ask, he still has answered it. He has seen that the request was unwise, so he has said no. He has answered it in the best way for us. We may ask for one thing believing that it is the thing we want. God in his wisdom may give us something else. We may see that God has given us what we really needed and wanted but not what we asked.

H. Pray With a Forgiving Spirit

This condition is important if we want our prayers to be answered. Jesus taught us to pray in Matthew 6:12: "Forgive us our debts, as we also have forgiven our debtors." Do we forgive others in the same way that we want God to forgive us? What is the promise that Jesus made in Matthew 6:14,15? _____
_____

To pray with an unforgiving heart is a sure way to close the doors of heaven to our prayers. It is a complete waste of time to pray that way. We must forgive others if we want God to forgive us.

I. Pray Without Being Showy or Repeating Useless Words

God hates fakes. He does not like people being showy. Jesus scolded the Pharisees for being fakes (Matthew 23:13-29). In the story of the Pharisee and the tax collector, which one did Jesus say was right in God's eyes? (Luke 18:9-14) _____
_____

Our prayers must be simple, direct, and sincere.

A sincere prayer given in faith does not repeat itself. Jesus taught against this in Matthew 6:7. This does not mean that we should not keep praying about some things. Jesus often would spend a night in prayer, or get up early to pray (Luke

9:28 and Mark 1:35). Jesus does say not to repeat useless words. God should not have to be begged.

IV. How Does The Holy Spirit Help In Prayer?

One of the great blessings for the Christian is the help of the Holy Spirit in prayer. Write Romans 8:26 in the blanks: _____

_____

Christians need this kind of help in prayer since we do not know what is best for us or the kingdom. We do not know what will happen tomorrow. We do not always know how to say in words exactly the feelings and desires of our heart.

For these and other reasons, our heavenly Father has given us his Holy Spirit to help us in prayer. The Holy Spirit takes what we ask and our praise and presents them in the right way to the throne of God. He also is a go-between for us with God. The Father, the Son, and the Holy Spirit are all part of prayer. The Christian's prayer is to God the Father, in the name of Christ, and with the help of the Holy Spirit. Prayer is a wonderful right that the Christian enjoys and should always use.

V. Has God Promised To Answer Prayer?

God does answer prayer! This is a proven fact in the Bible. Moses prayed and his prayer saved a nation from death (Exodus 32:14). Joshua prayed and the sun stood still and his enemies were killed by hailstones sent from heaven (Joshua 10:10-14). Hannah prayed and God gave her a son, Samuel (1 Samuel 1:9-20).

God's word is filled with the promises of answered prayer. Look up each of these passages of Scripture and tell what was promised:

1. 1 Peter 3:12: _____

2. James 1:5: _____

3. John 15:7: _____

If we will meet the "conditions" that God has given for prayer, we can be sure that our prayers will be heard and answered according to the will and wisdom of God.

Prayer

Answer True Or False:

_____ **1.** Man began to pray when God commanded him to pray.

_____ **2.** If we ask God anything at all, he will do it.

_____ **3.** The Holy Spirit has nothing to do with prayer.

_____ **4.** God does not listen to some prayers.

_____ **5.** God may answer prayer but still not give what was asked.

Answer The Following:

1. Prayer is made up of what two parts? _____

and _____

2. List three conditions for prayer to be effective:

a. _____

b. _____

c. _____

3. Give two reasons we should pray in Christ's name:

a. _____

b. _____

4. In your own words tell why you think we should pray:

_____

_____

5. Tell of some answers to prayer that you have seen:

_____

_____

Giving

In our previous lessons we have learned how to become a Christian. We have also learned how a Christian is to worship and to pray. This lesson will teach how to worship by giving.

The word "stewardship" is used to describe how people manage things. Christians must learn how to manage their time, talents, and money for the Lord. This lesson is about God's teaching on man's worship through giving of money. God's word has much to say about giving. There are some basic teachings on Christian giving. Examples of giving and God's promises to those who give will be studied in this chapter.

I. All Things Belong To God

This is the first and most basic teaching of giving. Moses told the children of Israel what God wanted them to do. In Deuteronomy 10:14 he wrote, "To the LORD your God belong the heavens, even the highest heavens, the earth and everything in it." David said the same thing in Psalm 24:1, "The earth is the LORD'S, and everything in it, the world, and all who live in it."

David also wrote about God's ownership of everything in Psalm 50:10-12. Turn to those verses and write as many things as you can that God says are his:

_____

_____

Now, turn to the following verses and tell the different things that belong to God:
1. Haggai 2:8: _____

_____

2. Ezekiel 29:9: _____

_____

3. Leviticus 25:23:_____

_____

4. Exodus 19:5: _____

_____

5. Ezekiel 18:4: _____

81

6. 1 Corinthians 6:19,20: _____

_____

7. 1 Chronicles 29:11: _____

_____

II. Every Christian Is A Manager

The second teaching of Christian giving is that every Christian is a manager of what God has given to him. Jesus gave a story about money in Matthew 25:14-30. The servants in the story stand for Christ's followers. Each servant was given a certain amount of money and told to use it to help the king who gave it. Peter wrote in 1 Peter 4:10, "Each one should use whatever gift he has received to serve others, faithfully administering God's grace in its various forms."

A manager is a person who looks over or takes care of another person's property. He does not own it. He manages it for the real owner. Turn to 1 Corinthians 4:2 and write the verse in the blanks:_____

_____

_____

How you understand your money and God are clear in these two basic teachings. God owns all things. We manage the things that God gives to us. We own nothing! Everything we have comes directly or indirectly from God. We take care of the blessings that he has given to us. We are supposed to use these things the way the real owner—**God**—wants us to use them. Many Christians believe that their money belongs to them. The truth is that it all belongs to God and he allows us to use part of it for ourselves. Do you think that this should change the way we treat money and the way we treat God?

III. God Gives In Many Ways

Not only does God own everything, but as Paul says, "Command those who are rich in this present world not to be arrogant nor to put their hope in wealth, which is so uncertain, but to put their hope in God, who richly provides us with everything for our enjoyment" (1 Timothy 6:17). Turn to James 1:17 and fill in the missing words: "Every _____ and _____ gift is from above, coming down from the _____ of the heavenly lights, who does not _____ like shifting shadows."
Look up the following verses and write the blessing that God has given us:

82

1. John 3:16:_____

_____

2. Romans 6:23:_____

_____

3. Ephesians 2:8: _____

_____

4. 1 Peter 1:18,19:: _____

_____

5. James 1:5:_____

_____

6. 2 Corinthians 8:9:_____

_____

7. Ephesians 5:2: _____

_____

8. Acts 17:30:_____

_____

IV. How People Gave In The Old Testament

A. How Individuals Gave

Bringing a gift or an offering to God is as old as the history of man. Genesis chapter 4 records the first offering. The first giving was done by the sons of Adam and Eve.

1. *How Cain and Abel gave*

Genesis 4:3-7 does not say that God had commanded Cain and Abel to bring sacrifices to him. Hebrews 11:4 says, "By faith Abel offered God a better sacrifice than Cain did. By faith he was commended as a righteous man, when God spoke well of his offerings. And by faith he still speaks, even though he is dead."

Cain was a farmer, so he brought some fruit from the ground for his offering. Abel brought the best parts of his best sheep because he was a shepherd. God accepted Abel's offering but he did not accept Cain's. We do not know why. Maybe it was the wrong type of offering. Maybe it was selfish of Cain or given with the wrong attitude. Whatever the case, we see in this story the first example of bringing a gift to God in worship.

2. *How Noah gave*

When Noah came out of the ark after the flood, the first thing he did was to build an altar to Jehovah. He took some of every clean animal and every clean bird to offer them to God as his offering. This showed his thanksgiving and worship of God for saving him and his family. God was pleased with this offering and promised never to destroy the earth again with water. Turn to Genesis 8:20-22 and write what God told Noah in your own words: _____

_____

_____

_____

3. *How Abraham gave*

By the time of Abraham we find something new in giving. Abraham still offered animal sacrifices to God. He also gave "tithes" (or ten percent). In Genesis 14:18-20 is recorded Abraham's meeting with Melchizedek. Abraham had rescued Lot after he had been captured by the four kings. In the rescue, Abraham had taken a lot of goods from those kings. As he returned, he met Melchizedek, king of Salem, who was also a priest for the Most High God. As the priest blessed Abraham, Abraham gave the priest a tenth of all his goods. We don't know if God had commanded Abraham to do this. Later giving by Abraham's family may mean that God had taught Abraham about tithing (giving ten percent).

4. *How Jacob gave*

Abraham's grandson, Jacob, also was a "tither." As Jacob left his home on his way to Uncle Laban's, he spent the night at Bethel. There he dreamed of the ladder which went from earth to heaven. In the morning, he made a promise to God. Fill in the missing words in the blanks from Genesis 28:20-22: "Then Jacob made a vow, saying, 'If God will be with me and will watch over me on this journey I am taking and will _____ me food to eat and clothes to wear so that I _____ safely to my father's house, then the LORD will be my God and this stone that I have set up as a pillar will be _____ house, and of all that you give me I will give you a _____.'"

It seems that God was not upset with Jacob's promise. He seemed to be pleased because God continued to bless Jacob with material things and in spiritual ways his whole life. Jacob lived up to his promise also. These are examples of giving by individuals during the time of the Fathers (or "Patriarchal Age"). As we move into the time of Moses, we will find that God's rules for giving are much clearer.

B. How Giving Was Done Under the Law of Moses

When God gave the law to Moses on Mount Sinai, he made "tithing" the main teaching about giving for the Children of Israel. He not only commanded one tithe, but possibly three!

1. *The first tithe commanded*

Read Leviticus 27:30-33 and answer these questions:

a. To whom did the one-tenth belong? _____

b. What happened when a person wanted to keep back part of his one-tenth?____

_____

c. Besides the crops, what else was part of giving one-tenth? _____

_____

d. Could the owners pick out the good and bad animals?_____

_____

e. Who commanded these rules? _____

The first tenth was to go to help the Levites (tribe of priests). The tithe from the other eleven tribes was thought of as property for the Levites. This was because they did not receive any part of the land when Israel moved into Canaan. God's teaching to Moses was: "I give to the Levites all the tithes in Israel as their inheritance in return for the work they do while serving at the Tent of Meeting" (Numbers 18:21).

When the tribe of Levi received the tenth (tithe) from the other eleven tribes, they in turn were to give a tenth of what they had received to Aaron to help his family and the priests. They did not receive any land either. Jehovah spoke to Moses in Numbers 18:26-28: "Speak to the Levites and say to them: 'When you receive from the Israelites the tithe I give you as your inheritance, you must present a tenth of that tithe as the LORD'S offering. Your offering will be reckoned to you as grain from the threshing floor or juice from the winepress. In this way you also will present an offering to the LORD from all the tithes you receive from the Israelites. From these tithes you must give the LORD'S portion to Aaron the priest.'" We see God's care for his own. He cared for the eleven tribes by giving them land when they moved into Canaan. He cared for the Levites and the priests as they served at the Tent of Meeting (Tabernacle).

2. *The second tithe*

After the first tithe had been taken, Deuteronomy shows that a second tithe was to be given out of the remaining nine-tenths! This second tithe was to be used for a holy meal to be eaten as an act of worship wherever God said. Later, the place was Jerusalem because that is where the Temple was. This second tenth was used to pay for the many feasts and meals which Jehovah required from his people. (See Deuteronomy 12:17-19 and 14:22-27.) If an Israelite lived too far away to carry his tenth with him, he could change it into money and then buy the food in Jerusalem.

3. *The third tithe*

Deuteronomy 14:28,29 may be teaching a third tithe! In the blanks below, write these two verses: _____
_____
_____

For whom was this tithe given?_____

What would the Lord God do? _____
_____
_____

In summary, the Law of Moses required every Jew to give one-tenth of all his crops and herds each year to help the Levites as they served God at the Tent of Meeting. The Levites tithed to the priests so that they might live. The eleven tribes were to give a second tenth each year for the holy feasts as they worshiped at the Tent of Meeting and later the Temple. Then, every three years they gave a "poor tithe." This went to the Levites, widows, orphans and the poor people (see Deuteronomy 26:12,13).

V. God Blesses Giving Ten Percent

God's blessings are always balanced with what he wants from man. At first, it seems that God had required a lot of giving from the Children of Israel. But God has never asked us to give to him more than what he has given to us first. God told Israel if they would obey his commands that he would bless them greatly. Fill in the missing words from Deuteronomy 28:3-6: "You will be _____ in the city and _____ in the country. The _____ of your womb will be blessed, and the crops of your land and the young of your _____—the calves of your herds and the lambs of your flocks. Your basket and your kneading trough will be _____. You will be blessed when you come in and _____ when you go out."

Solomon teaches in Proverbs 3:9,10: "Honor the LORD with your wealth, with the firstfruits of all your crops; then your barns will be filled to overflowing, and your vats will brim over with new wine."

Perhaps the best known verses of God's promises to Israel for giving are found in Malachi 3:10-12. Read those verses and list three blessings that God promised Israel:

a. _____

b. _____

c. _____

God is as loving and as giving today as he was in Israel's day (Hebrews 13:8).

Giving

Answer The Following Questions:

1. What is the first teaching of Christian giving?_____
_____

2. What is the second teaching of Christian giving?_____
_____

3. What is "tithing?"_____
_____

Fill In The Blanks:

1. For an offering Cain brought _____ and Abel brought
_____.

2. List four things that the Bible says God owns:

    a._____   c._____
    b._____   d._____

3. Melchizedek was the king of _____ and _____ of the Most
High God.

4. What do these verses say that God gives to us?
    a. James 1:5:_____
    b. Romans 6:23:_____
    c. 1 Timothy 6:17:_____

5. Israel gave the first tenth to the _____ because they had no
_____.

6. Explain Malachi 3:10-12 in your own words:_____
_____
_____

Giving In The New Testament

Giving is taught often in the New Testament. The Bible has far more to say about the right use of money than it does about baptism and the Lord's Supper combined! One third of our Lord's parables were about money. One verse in every six in the books of Matthew, Mark and Luke talks about money!

I. What Giving Means

Many people fail to give as they should mainly because they do not understand what giving really means. Once a sincere Christian sees the full meaning of this part of the Christian life, it becomes a joy and a blessing to give.

A. It Is a Gift of Grace

2 Corinthians 8:7 says: "But just as you excel in everything—in faith, in speech, in knowledge, in complete earnestness and in your love for us—see that you also excel in this grace of giving." Giving is a gift! Like the "fruit of the Spirit" in Galatians 5:22, giving is part of what the Holy Spirit produces in our lives.

Man by nature is selfish. The first law of life is "take care of yourself." Man thinks of himself, his family, his needs and desires first. Only as we become like God do we begin to put God and others before ourselves.

We learn to be unselfish and to give just as we learn other things in the Christian life. When we find ourselves not able to give freely, we should ask God to help us have the right attitude about money. We should ask to use money the way that Christ would. To be able to give as Jesus gave is a spiritual goal for every Christian.

B. It Is an Act of Worship

Many Christians think of offering time as something just to pay the bills. Giving is more than that. Instead of being a burden, the offering is a beautiful act of worship to God.

God required all male Jews to attend the three main feasts each year: Unleavened Bread (Passover), Weeks (Pentecost) and Feast of Tabernacles. When they came, God said in Deuteronomy 16:16,17: "Three times a year all your men must appear before the LORD your God at the place he will choose: at the Feast of Unleavened Bread, the Feast of Weeks and the Feast of Tabernacles. No man should appear before the LORD empty-handed: Each of you must bring a gift in proportion to the way the LORD your God has blessed you." These feasts were a part of their worship of Jehovah. He wanted them to bring an offering. This was an act of worship.

The same idea is taught in the New Testament. Turn to Acts 2:42 and write the verse in the blanks: _____

_____

_____

Along with teaching, prayer and breaking bread, Luke adds the idea of "sharing." This word is used in Romans 15:26 for "giving money." This sharing or giving by the New Testament church was thought by the Holy Spirit to be worship of God. Also, in 1 Corinthians 16:2, Paul teaches the church: "On the first day of every week, each one of you should set aside a sum of money in keeping with his income, saving it up, so that when I come no collections will have to be made." On the same day that they worshiped God in prayer, in Bible study and the Lord's Supper, they also worshiped by giving their offerings.

Christian giving as an act of worship is important because:
1. *Giving is something we must do.*
Too many people see Christian giving as a small part of a Christian's duty. A person gives when he feels like it and when it is easy. (Many people don't feel like giving very often.) God told Israel not to meet him with empty hands. The Christian today should feel the same need to give to God.

2. *Giving is worship to God.*
Giving is an act of worship to God! Many people give to help the preacher, to build a building or to pay bills. This can be a false idea. We should always be giving to God first. The money may be used for many things. But we should know in our heart as we worship that our gift is to God.

In the bread of the Lord's Supper we should see the body of Christ. In the cup of juice we should see the blood that Jesus gave for our sins. Perhaps the hand of Christ should be painted on the bottom of the offering plate! Then we would understand that our offering is given to Christ.

C. Giving Is an Act of Love

Love is the greatest power in the world. All Christian service should be done mostly out of love. Christian giving should also be done because of love. Write 2 Corinthians 8:24 in the blanks: _____

_____

Paul was teaching the Christians at Corinth to give as an example for the other churches. Do you suppose that God wants proof of our love for him? Look up 1 John 3:18. How does John say that we can prove our love?_____

_____

God can often tell more about our love for him from what we put in the offering plate than in what we say.

It seems right that the offering plates are often placed on the same table as the Lord's Supper. In the Lord's Supper we see the greatest picture or proof of God's love for us. In the offering plate we should see at least one proof of our love for God. This table should be a table of love for every Christian.

In summary, Christian giving is a gift of grace that God grows in us through his Holy Spirit. It is an act of worshiping God. It is not a small part of our Christian life. It is an act of obedience to God. It is an act of love for God in our hearts because he first loved us. Write 1 John 4:19 in the blanks: _____

_____

II. Why We Should Give

A. Giving Can Help the Work of the Kingdom

We live in a material world. It takes money to carry on God's work in this world. It takes money to help those who preach the good news. Paul praised the Philippian church for their giving. They helped him preach the good news. How did they help him? (Turn to Philippians 4:14-16 for your answer.) _____

_____

Who helped Paul when he preached at Corinth? (Find your answer in 2 Corinthians 11:9.) _____

_____

How else did they help Paul? (Philippians 4:18 will tell you.) _____

It takes money to care for widows and orphans, to build church buildings, to send missionaries and to print Bibles. Giving helps the work of the kingdom.

B. Giving Can Help the Christian Grow

This is the first purpose for Christian giving. Why does God ask us to give? The more we give, the more we will be like him. It is true that God owns everything. If he wanted to provide for all the needs of the church, he could. But this would not help us grow to be like God. All of God's laws and rules are for our good. How did Paul tell the Corinthians that God would bless them in their giving? (2 Corinthians 9:11) _____

_____

What did Jesus say in Matthew 6:21? _____

_____

When we give to something we usually care more about it. This is because money is a big part of our life. Jesus knew that if we put our money into the kingdom of God our hearts would be there too. God wants us, not our money. But, he uses money to reach our hearts. Jesus teaches that money is a test or a way that God can tell if we can receive spiritual blessings.

Fill in the missing words from Luke 16:10-12:
"Whoever can be _____ with very little can also be _____ with much, and whoever is _____ with very little will also be _____ with much. So if you have not been _____ in handling worldly wealth, who will trust you with true _____? And if you have not been _____ with someone else's property, who will give you _____ of your own?"

Jesus says that if we have not been faithful in our material riches, then we will not receive the true riches. True riches are spiritual riches from God. If we do learn how to use our material riches in the right way, then God will give us those spiritual blessings. A true Christian is not selfish with "his" money.

God requires us to give so that we can:
1. *Have a right attitude about money.*
The Lord wants us to see that money is our servant, not our boss. When we understand that God gives us material blessings to be used for God and for good, then money becomes our servant. Money can be used as a blessing in a thousand ways

when it is our servant. But, when money becomes the boss, terrible things can happen. (An example of this is the story of the rich young man in Mark 10:17-31.)

2. *Become like God by being unselfish.*

Being selfish and wanting what others have is the opposite of what God is. God loved us so much that he gave us his Son. God has no selfishness in him. He asks us to give so that we will grow up to be like him. The more we study the Christian life, the more we learn that loving and giving are at the very heart of it all.

C. Giving Can Help Us Be Responsible to God

Turn to Matthew 16:27 and write the verse in the blanks: _____
_____

Paul repeated the words of Jesus when he wrote: "For we must all appear before the judgment seat of Christ, that each one may receive what is due him for the things done while in the body, whether good or bad" (2 Corinthians 5:10). Turn to Hebrews 9:27 and fill in the missing words: "Just as man is _____ to die once, and after that to face _____."

The Bible tells us that we will give an account of what we have done on earth. God will look at our giving as well as our other Christian service. God was upset with the Jews for their greed and blamed them for robbing him. Turn to Malachi 3:8,9 to find out how God told the Jews they were robbing him. How were they robbing God? Give your answer in the blanks. _____
_____

How do you think that God will feel about a Christian who robs him? Turn to Colossians 3:5. How serious is it to God that we selfishly want more and more?
_____

Is it possible that a Christian who has received every blessing imaginable from God would rob him by keeping back money which belongs to God? This is not be-ing thankful. It is really stealing! We must learn to give in the right way and with the right attitude. Why? How would we answer God at the judgment?

If we have been faithful in the use of money on earth, we will hear God say, "'Well done, good and faithful servant! You have been faithful with a few things; I will put you in charge of many things. Come and share your master's happiness!'" (Matthew 25:23).

We have seen that giving is a Christian "grace" or gift. We have also seen that giving is part of our worship of God. The next question is, How much should I give?

III. How A Christian Should Give

Man is not able to set the standard or measurement for giving. Some who give 1% of their money believe that they are being generous. Others who give 20% feel that they are giving what God expects. Both types of people are not right. The church would be like Israel as Judges 17:6 says, "In those days Israel had no king; everyone did as he saw fit."

A. God Is the Only One Who Can Say How to Give

In the Bible there is no limit to what a Christian can give. The sky is the limit! The Bible does teach a starting point for Christian giving. In Lesson 10 we see that the Jew in the Old Testament gave a first "tithe" (ten percent) to help the Lord's work (Leviticus 27:30-32; Numbers 18:21-28). He also gave a second ten percent in worship to God (Deuteronomy 12:17-19). Some Jews would give even more! (Malachi 3:8).

B. More Is Asked of Christians Than of the Jews

The New Testament asks the Christian to give freely (Romans 12:8). Christians should give as if they are planting a lot and happily (2 Corinthians 9:6,7). What did Jesus tell his followers in Matthew 5:20? _____

_____

_____

We can be certain that God does not ask less of us than he did of the Jews. Surely the Christian should begin with tithing (giving ten percent). Then we can go above that as much as our love for God leads and the needs allow. We as Christians have a greater agreement with God (Hebrews 8:6). We have better promises in that agreement (2 Peter 1:4). We have a greater mission to tell the good news to the whole world (Matthew 28:19,20; Mark 16:15,16). The needs today are greater. We must give more than the Jews did to be pleasing to Christ and to reach the world with the gospel.

Giving In The New Testament

Fill In The Blanks:

1. 2 Corinthians 9:6,7: "Remember this: Whoever sows sparingly will also _____ sparingly, and whoever sows _____ will also reap generously. Each man should give what he has decided in his _____ to give, not reluctantly or under _____, for God loves a cheerful giver."

2. 1 Corinthians 16:2: "On the _____ day of every week, each one of you should set aside a sum of _____ in keeping with his _____, saving it up, so that when I come no collections will have to be made."

3. Matthew 5:20: "For I tell you that unless your _____ surpasses that of the Pharisees and the _____ of the law, you will certainly not _____ the kingdom of heaven."

Answer The Following:

1. Giving is a "grace." What does that mean? _____

_____

2. List three reasons Christians should give:

    a. _____

    b. _____

    c. _____

3. Explain how giving is a part of worshiping God. _____

_____

4. Give all the reasons you can think of that a Christian should give more than the Jews did in the Old Testament. _____

_____

The Mission Of The Church

I. The Church Has A Mission

The purpose of the church is given in Matthew 28:19,20. Turn to these verses and answer the following questions. What is the first thing that we are told to do?

_____

_____

Into Whom are Christ's followers to be baptized? _____

_____

What are the followers to be taught? _____

_____

_____

These verses tell us the mission of the church. This is the reason that there is a church. Its mission is to bring people to Christ and to build them into the image of Christ. This "work" includes the whole world. It will continue as long as there is one lost soul or until the Lord returns. We can say that the preaching of the Good News to the world is the mission of the church.

II. What "Missions" Means

The word used the most for reaching the world is "missions." What do we mean by "missions?" The dictionary tells us that the noun "mission" is "sending or being sent to do special service;—a calling, especially to preach and tell about a religion." The word "missions" is not used in the New Testament. It is a word that comes from the Latin language. A "missionary" is "one who is sent on a mission." It is the same as the word "apostle." The word "missions" is a modern word for the great purpose of the church—preaching the good news to the whole world.

III. Christianity Has A Missionary Heart

The questions are often asked, Why send missionaries to other countries? Don't they already have their own religion? Why should we send millions of dollars and thousands of missionaries to make the people in other countries Christians? Wouldn't it be better not to bother them with this teaching? If Christianity is just a religion among many religions and if Christ is a Savior among many saviors—there is no reason to go. If this is true, there would be other ways by which we could be saved!

The reason for world missions is in the very heart of Christianity. There are at least two major things that make Christianity missionary minded.

A. Christianity Claims to Be the Only True Religion

This claim caused problems with the Romans in the first 100 years after Jesus' death. It still causes problems today! The Romans would have let the church be one of the religions of the empire. But they did not like the way Christians claimed to have the only true religion. They did not like Christians saying that all other religions were false.

There is no doubt that the New Testament claims it has the true "good news." Jehovah is not a God; he is the only God. Turn to 1 Corinthians 8:4 and write the verse in the blanks: _____

_____

Jesus Christ is not *a* Savior; he is the only Savior. What did Peter say about which name could save? Turn to Acts 4:12 and write your answer. _____

_____

This is why Christianity has a missionary heart.

B. Christianity Sees Everyone as a
Sinner and in Need of Being Saved by Christ

Salvation means to be saved from sin and from what happens when you sin. Sin has made the whole world enemies of God. Who has sinned according to Romans 3:23? _____ Only in Christ can people be saved from sin. This belief was the loving reason the early Christians left their homes and families to face terrible times, persecution and death to tell this saving message to those dying in sin. These two beliefs of the church show that Christianity has a missionary heart.

C. Christ as the Head of the Church Was the Greatest Missionary

A third reason for missions is the example of Christ. Jesus taught missions. He commanded missions. He himself was the greatest missionary in history! What does John say about him in 1 John 4:9?_____

_____

Jesus Christ was "one sent on a mission." He was a missionary. He was sent from heaven to earth with a purpose. Why did Jesus say he came? (Luke 19:10) _____

_____

Whose will had he come to do? (John 6:38) _____

_____

Jesus' purpose was the same as any missionary today. He was sent to save those who were lost (Ephesians 2:1 says, "As for you, you were dead in your transgressions and sins"). When we do mission work today, we are continuing the great plan that our Lord began! Jesus left heaven and came to earth to make salvation possible for everyone.

IV. What Moves A Person To Be A Missionary

A "motive" is something that moves a person to act. It forces a person to do something. What are the right motives for going as a missionary or for sending others? There are many motives which speak to the heart of true believers but we will look at a few.

A. Knowing What We Have in Christ and the World's Great Need for Him

When we truly see Christ and understand what he has done for us, we can never be happy until we share him with others. One of the greatest motives for preaching the good news to the world is wanting to share the Water of Life with those who most need him.

If we will look at the cross of Calvary until we see the true meaning of what Christ did, we can never be selfish with the message of love shown by Christ.

This is the meaning of John 3:16. God so loved that he gave his Son to save lost people. Jesus loved and gave his life for them. Turn to Romans 5:6-8 and put these verses in your own words: _____

_____

Shouldn't we today as God's children continue to look for lost brothers and sisters of ours? Shouldn't we keep looking for every child of God until all are found and brought back safely to their heavenly Father?

B. The Command of Christ

Jesus not only taught and showed how to be a missionary; he commanded missions. Matthew, Mark, Luke, John and Acts record the command from Christ for missions. Give the meaning of each of the following verses in your own words:

1. Matthew 28:18-20: _____

2. Mark 16:15,16: _____

3. Luke 24:46-49:_____

4. John 20:21: _____

5. Acts 1:8: _____

For anyone who has not accepted Jesus as Lord of their life, these commands don't mean anything. But if you have given yourself to the authority of Christ, you will be truly happy in doing his will. You will be happy to be an "ambassador" (one sent for a king or president) for Christ. What does Christ have us do for him? (Turn to 2 Corinthians 5:18-20 for your answer.) _____

_____

_____

Christians should obey the Lord's command simply because of who he is! He is the head of the church. He is the Lord of Lords and King of Kings. It should be a happy honor to obey the Lord. His command should be obeyed because he said to do it.

Many Christians would not think of leaving baptism out of Christ's command for missions. But, they would leave out the part that says, "Go into all the world and preach the good news to all creation" (Mark 16:15). The same Lord who commanded baptism also commanded that we go into the whole world! Christians do not have the right to obey part of Christ's command and forget the rest.

In 2 Corinthians 5:10, Paul talks about going to stand before Christ to be judged. What does he say in verse 11?_____

_____

_____

Paul did not have a choice about preaching the good news. The Lord had spoken!

Fill in the missing words from 1 Corinthians 9:16: "Yet when I _____ the gospel, I cannot _____, for I am _____ to preach. Woe to me if I do _____ preach the gospel!" Christians today must have this holy fear of God so that we can tell the good news to the world. How would we face Christ, the Judge?

C. Being Thankful for Being Saved

The sinner has been healed from sin by God's grace. He should never stop telling the world of this saving grace through Christ, our great doctor! This should be our great reason for missions. We are saved to save others. Paul said in Romans 1:14,15: "I am obligated both to Greeks and non-Greeks, both to the wise and the foolish. That is why I am so eager to preach the gospel also to you who are at Rome."

V. Who Is Responsible For Missions

Jesus gave the great command to go into all the world to the apostles. But, it was not just for them to do. The early church clearly understood that it was every believer's job.

Philip was one of the first deacons. He became famous for preaching the good news (see Acts 21:8). When the church was scattered from Jerusalem following the death of Stephen, it says, "Those who had been scattered preached the word wherever they went" (Acts 8:4). This was not the apostles because they were still back in Jerusalem (Acts 8:1). These were the members of the church. Every believer was a preacher! Fill in the missing words from Revelation 22:17: "The _____ and the bride say, '_____!' And let him who hears say, '_____!' Whoever is thirsty, let him come; and _____ wishes, let him take the _____ gift of the water of life." Everyone of us who believe and accept the Lord are to immediately begin calling others to the Water of Life.

Who is to do missionary work? Every Christian is. Every one of us should feel the need to go and to send others. We should first go to our own neighborhoods. The Lord may also call us to other countries. If we don't go to other countries, we should at least do our best to give to those who do go. The Lord won't ask at the judgment, "What did your church do for missions?" But he will ask, "What did you do?" Until each believer feels the need to tell the good news personally, the world will not be won to Christ.

VI. How Missions Are Done

The book of Acts tells us how missions are done. God has given the church the best book on missions.

A. Where to Preach

Paul often chose places to preach, but let the Holy Spirit guide him. There is a plan for each of Paul's three preaching trips (journeys).

Paul used the Roman roads wherever he could. Why? Because these roads tied important cities together. Paul also chose cities because they were important for buying and selling. They were important because of politics and schools. One of the cities, Antioch of Syria, had about 500,000 people! It was the third city around the Mediterranean Sea in importance. It was also the home of the Roman government in Syria.

The small island of Cyprus was an excellent starting point for preaching the good news because it was at the center of business. Ephesus was the shopping and political capital for all the area called Asia. Paul spent almost three years at Ephesus. He then let the local church do the preaching of Christ to the areas around them.

B. Preaching and Prayer

Paul started a church by preaching and teaching (you can see this in Acts 14:1; 17:1-3, 17; 18:5; 19:8,9). Paul knew of no other way for lost people to be saved than by preaching. Write 1 Corinthians 1:21 in the blanks:

_____

_____

How important to faith is preaching? (Turn to Romans 10:17 for your answer.)

_____

_____

Fill in the missing word from Romans 10:14,15: "How, then, can they call on the one they have not _____ in? And how can they believe in the one of whom they have not _____? And how can they hear without someone _____ to them? And how can they preach unless they are _____? As it is written, 'How beautiful are the feet of those who bring good news!'" For Paul, this was the way that God wanted him to bring people to Christ and to start churches.

Prayer was another important way that Paul started churches. In all of his letters, he asked for the prayers of other Christians and told how he was praying for them. He asked for prayers for the good news to spread (2 Thessalonians 3:1). He asked for prayers that he would be saved from great dangers (2 Corinthians 1:10,11). He asked for prayers that the Jewish Christians would accept the gifts from the non-Jews (Romans 15:30,31). He also asked for prayers that he could preach the good news (Colossians 4:3). He even told his converts that he was always praying for them (Philippians 1:3-5).

Paul needed his personal prayer life in order to keep going in his life. He prayed because it always brought results for the kingdom of God.

C. Paul Started "Independent" Churches

By "independent" is meant that the church was able to organize itself, able to pay its own way and able to preach the good news to others.

1. *Able to organize itself*
From the book of Acts we learn that Paul did not watch the churches for a long time. He helped them to pick leaders and went on. This is what he did on his first missionary trip. Paul and Barnabas started churches in Antioch of Pisidia, Iconium, Lystra and Derbe. What did they do on the way back home? (Find your answer in Acts 14:23.) _____

_____

_____

Acts 20 tells us that there were elders at the church at Ephesus. (See Philippians 1:1.) Titus is told to pick elders in every city on the island of Crete (Titus 1:5). These local leaders continued to teach and lead the churches while Paul moved to another place.

2. *Able to pay its own way*
This was another way that Paul helped the churches to be "independent." It meant that the church would be able to take care of its own money for the Lord. There are examples of one church helping another when it was in need. One example is Antioch helping the church at Jerusalem (Acts 11:27-30). Paul collected gifts from Asia and Greece for the poor Christians in Judea (1 Corinthians 16:1,2; Romans 15:31).

Paul taught the churches in Galatia to help those who taught them the word. Fill in the missing words from Galatians 6:6: "Anyone who receives

_____ in the word must _____ all good things with his _____." Paul was probably talking about money when he told Timothy, "The elders who direct the affairs of the church well are worthy of double honor, especially those whose work is preaching and teaching" (1 Timothy 5:17). Teaching beginning churches to pay their own way is important. If they don't learn this, it can rob them of growing in faith and some great blessings from the Lord.

3. *Able to preach the good news to others*
This idea is tied in with the other two. If a church is not able to organize itself and not able to pay its own way, how can it be able to send others to preach the good news? Paul said in 1 Thessalonians 1:8 "The Lord's message rang out from you not only in Macedonia and Achaia—your faith in God has become known everywhere. Therefore we do not need to say anything about it." In most cases, Christians in other countries are able to win their own people to the Lord faster than a missionary can. Paul taught those early churches a vital lesson. When he taught them to win those around them, he was teaching that every Christian needed to do the work of the ministry. It is not for a few paid ministers! This is how to teach the whole church to minister (see Ephesians 4:11,12).

The Mission Of The Church

Answer The Following:

1. How does Christianity have a missionary heart? _____
_____

2. Why did Paul choose cities to start churches? _____
_____

3. What do you think is the greatest reason for doing mission work? _____
_____

4. Give three ways that a church can be "independent":
    a. _____
    b. _____
    c. _____

5. Was the great command in Matthew 28:19,20 for missions given only to the
apostles? Why or why not? _____
_____

Explain These Words:

1. Missionary: _____
_____

2. Mission: _____
_____

3. Religion: _____
_____

The Second Coming Of The Lord

There is no teaching more important than our Lord's second coming. His first coming was to save people. The second coming will be to take those who have been saved (through faith and obedience) back to heaven. Write Hebrews 9:28 in the blanks: _____

_____

_____

The importance of this teaching is seen in how many verses in the Bible talk about the second coming. Someone has said that almost one verse out of five in the whole New Testament talks about the Lord's return. Four of Jesus' parables teach about it! One example of this is in Paul's first letter to the Thessalonians. Paul ends each chapter by talking about the second coming (1 Thessalonians 1:10; 2:19; 3:13; 4:14-18; 5:23). Paul spoke about it so often that the people thought that Jesus was coming soon. One of the reasons he wrote 2 Thessalonians was to explain what he meant by his first letter to them.

We can't read the New Testament without seeing how important this teaching was to the early church.

I. Jesus' Second Coming Is Sure

A. Some Doubt His Return

Nothing is taught more clearly in the New Testament than that Christ will come again. This is the great hope of all true Christians. But there are some who do not believe that he is coming again, in person, to the earth. Peter told us about this in 2 Peter 3: 3, 4. Turn to those verses and fill in the missing words: "First of all, you must understand that in the last days _scoffers_ will come, scoffing and following their own evil _desires_. They will say, 'Where is this "coming" he _promised_? Ever since our fathers died, _everything_ goes on as it has since the beginning of _creation_.'" Because the

107

Lord has not come, many have thought that he will not come. The evil servant had the same wrong idea in the parable Jesus told in Matthew 24:45-51.

The Bible teaches that Christ returned in the form of the Holy Spirit on the Day of Pentecost (Acts 2). Remember what Jesus said in Matthew 28:20? "And surely I am with you always, to the very end of the age." Write John 14:23 in the blanks:

_____

_____

Christ has been with his church through the Holy Spirit all the time! The second coming in the Bible is when Jesus comes again in person for everybody to see.

B. Some Proof That He Is Coming Again

There are many proofs that Jesus will come to earth again. What does Hebrews 10:37 say about the way that Jesus will come again? _____

_____

_____

The Old Testament told about his second coming even before his first coming! Daniel said, "In my vision at night I looked, and there before me was one like a son of man, coming with the clouds of heaven. He approached the Ancient of Days and was led into his presence"(Daniel 7:13). There aren't very many verses in the Old Testament about the second coming. The New Testament makes this great event much clearer. There are at least four witnesses or proofs for the second coming:

1. *Jesus promised he will return.*
How did he tell the Jewish leaders he would come in Matthew 26:64?_____

_____

What does Jesus say that people will do at his coming? (Matthew 24:30)_____

_____

What is Jesus' promise in John 14:3? _____

_____

What did Jesus say would and would not be destroyed? (Matthew 24:35) _____

_____

Many years after Jesus had gone back to heaven, he spoke through John in Revelation 22:12. What did he promise in that verse? _____

John says in Revelation 22:20, "He who testifies to these things says, 'Yes, I am coming soon.' Amen. Come, Lord Jesus." Jesus said that he will come again. We can be sure that Christ will keep his word.

2. *The angels said he will return.*

The apostles stood on the Mount of Olives watching the Lord go up into heaven. Suddenly, their minds were turned back to earth by two men—probably angels—in white clothes. "'Men of Galilee,' they said, 'why do you stand here looking into the sky? This same Jesus, who has been taken from you into heaven, will come back in the same way you have seen him go into heaven.'" (Acts 1:11). The Bible tells us that the angels will come with Jesus when he returns (Matthew 24:31, for example). Certainly they should know about it and we can trust their witness.

3. *The apostles said he will return.*

The apostle Peter is very strong when he talks about the second coming. He answered those who said it would not happen (2 Peter 3:1-14). Peter tells us that the Lord is not slow in keeping his promise to return. He is being patient because he doesn't want anybody to be lost. He would like to see everybody change their heart and life. Turn to 2 Peter 3:10 and write the verse in your own words:

_____

_____

_____

(Take the time and look up these verses too: Acts 3:19-21; 1 Peter 1:3-13; 4:12, 13; 5:4. You may wish to make a list of what these verses say.) Who does John say will see the Lord? (Revelation 1:7) _____

_____

What do we need to do so that we will not be afraid when Jesus comes again? (1 John 2:28) _____

_____

What will the children of God see at the second coming? (1 John 3:2) _____

_____

The apostle Paul taught more about the second coming than the other apostles. He was happy about Jesus' return! He called the coming of Jesus "our hope." 1 Thessalonians 5:2 says that the day of the Lord will come like a "___thief___ in the night." How will we know when the Lord will return? Paul tells us in 1 Thessalonians 4:16. _____ (A good project or assignment would be to make a list of what is taught about the second coming from the following verses: Hebrews 9:27,28; Acts 17:30,31; Romans 2:16; 8:16-25; 13:11; 1 Corinthians 1:7; 4:5; 11:26; 15:23, 50-52; Philippians 2:16; 3:20; Colossians 3:1-4; 1 Thessalonians 1:9,10; 2:19; 3:11-13; 2 Thessalonians 1:7-12; 2:1-10; 2 Timothy 4:6-8; Titus 2:13; Revelation 6:12-17; 14:14,15; 16:15-21; 20:7-15.).

4. *The Lord's Supper says he will return.*
We think of the Lord's Supper as a time for remembering the cross. But the Lord's Supper also is for thinking about the second coming. Write 1 Corinthians 11:26 in the blanks: _____
_____
_____

Each Lord's day, as we think about the cross and the love of God when he gave Jesus, we should also look to the future. We should think about Jesus' promise to come again. We should tell one another that we are one week closer to the Lord's return! This should make us happy and keep us strong in the faith till he returns. Time is really short. The Lord's Supper is a good time to think about the lost and their need for the Savior too.

With these proofs that Jesus will come again, we can agree with Peter when he said, "We did not follow cleverly invented stories when we told you about the power and coming of our Lord Jesus Christ, but we were eyewitnesses of his majesty" (2 Peter 1:16). What else does Peter tell us to do to be ready? (1 Peter 1:13) _____
_____
_____

II. How Jesus Will Come Again

The Bible gives many details about the way that Jesus will return. The following are a few of those teachings on his coming:

A. Everyone Will See Him

How did the angels say that Jesus will return? (Acts 1:11) _____
_____

In your own words tell how Jesus went up to heaven (Luke 24:50,51; Acts 1:9,10): _____
_____
_____

110

The Bible says that Jesus will return in the same way. Again, who will see Jesus? (Revelation 1:7) _____

_____

You will not have to guess about his coming! What does Matthew 24:27 have to say? _____

_____

Those who are still living on earth when he returns will see him!

B. He Will Come With the Clouds

Clouds have always had a special part in God's plan to save us. God came down onto Mount Sinai in a cloud (Exodus 24:16). He also came down in a cloud when Jesus met with Moses and Elijah in Matthew 17:5. Israel was led through the wilderness by a cloud during the day and by a pillar of fire during the night (Exodus 13:21). Turn to Psalm 104:3. How does God use clouds? _____

_____ No _____

Jesus left on a cloud. He will return on a cloud. Fill in the missing words from Matthew 24:30: "At that time the _____ of the Son of Man will appear in the _____, and all the nations of the earth will mourn. They will see the Son of Man coming on the _____ of the sky, with power and great _____." The clouds should help us remember Jesus' promise to return the same way that he went back to heaven.

C. He Will Come in Glory With the Angels

Matthew 25:31 says, "When the Son of Man comes in his glory, and all the angels with him, he will sit on his throne in heavenly glory." When Jesus comes again it will be the victory march of a King who has won the battle! (1 Thessalonians 4:16). 2 Thessalonians 1:6,7 says, "God is just: He will pay back trouble to those who trouble you and give relief to you who are troubled, and to us as well. This will happen when the Lord Jesus is revealed from heaven in blazing fire with his powerful angels." Jesus came the first time as a baby in Bethlehem. He came quietly and not even noticed by most people. The second time he will be King and the whole earth will know it! The first time he came as a servant. The second time he will come in glory! Paul says that Christ's coming will be announced by the trumpet of God. What does he call it in 1 Corinthians 15:52?_____

_____

_____

The archangel shouts (1 Thessalonians 4:16) and the trumpet blows. (See John 5:28,29 where Jesus tells us how the dead will be raised.) 1 Thessalonians 4:17 says, "We who are still alive and are left will be caught up together with them in the clouds to meet the Lord in the air. And so we will be with the Lord forever."

D. He Will Come While Nature Changes

The earth itself will make some changes when the Creator returns. Possibly it will be like Matthew 24:29 when the sun, moon and stars are changed. Romans 8:19-22 talks about everything that God has made wanting to be free from ruin. This is perhaps the new earth that Peter tells us about in 2 Peter 3:13. (See also Revelation 21:1.)

III. When Jesus Will Come Again

Ever since the day that Christ went back to the Father, men have been guessing the time of his return. The Christians in Thessalonica were so sure that he would come in their lifetime, that some quit working (2 Thessalonians 2 and 3).

The Bible is very clear that Jesus' second coming is sure. The one thing that is not told is the time of his return. The Lord settled the question of setting dates when he said, "No one knows about that day or hour, not even the angels in heaven, nor the Son, but only the Father." (Matthew 24:36; Mark 13:32). If the angels in heaven and the Son do not know, it is certain that no man knows! Jesus told the apostles in Acts 1:7, "It is not for you to know the times or dates the Father has set by his own authority." All that we need to know is how to be ready for the Lord's return.

IV. How We Should Live Because He Is Coming Again

Since Christ's return is sure, how should we live? It's obvious that if we believe that Jesus is coming back, it will have a great effect on the way we live and think. Some people only say that they believe in the second coming. They act like they don't care. The reason is that they really don't believe enough to live a different life. The Bible teaches that this teaching, truly believed, will cause many changes in our Christian life.

A. Christians Should Be Different From the World

Paul told Titus about God's grace: "It teaches us to say 'No' to ungodliness and worldly passions, and to live self-controlled, upright and godly lives in this present age" (Titus 2:12,13). Fill in the missing words from 2 Peter 3:11: "Since everything will be _____ in this way, what _____ of people ought you to be? You ought to live _____ and godly lives." John says almost the same things in 1 John 2:15-17. In your own words, tell what John has to say to us:

_____

_____

These verses tell us how we should live until the second coming. We cannot continue to cling to the things that God will destroy at the end of this world.

B. Christians Should Be Holy

Peter tells us, "So then, dear friends, since you are looking forward to this, make every effort to be found spotless, blameless and at peace with him" (2 Peter 3:14). Fill in the missing words from 1 John 3:2,3: "Dear friends, now we are _____ of God, and what we will be has not yet been made known. But we know that when he _____, we shall be like him, for we shall _____ him as he is. Everyone who has this _____ in him purifies himself, just as he is pure." (See also Titus 2:12,13.)

Knowing that Jesus will return is the reason for the way we act in all areas of Christian living. Turn to the following verses and tell how we are to live as holy people:

1. Philippians 1:10,11: _____

_____

2. 1 Thessalonians 5:2,6: _____

_____

3. Philippians 4:5: _____

_____

4. Hebrews 10:36,37: _____

_____

5. 1 Peter 5:4: _____

_____

C. Christians Should Be Watching

The New Testament calls the church to be watching for the Lord's return at least 50 times. Matthew 24:42 tells us, "Therefore keep watch, because you do not know on what day your Lord will come." Why does he tell us to watch in Matthew 25:13? _____

_____

(Here is another list of verses about "watching" that could be kept on a separate piece of paper for your own encouragement: Mark 13:37; 2 Peter 3:12; Luke 21:7-36; Philippians 3:20,21; 1 Corinthians 1:7; 1 Thessalonians 1:10; 2 Thessalonians 3:5.)

Watching for the Lord's second coming shows our faith. We believe that the Lord is coming. We watch and wait for him. Paul told Titus to live like he wanted the Lord to return (Titus 2:13). If we truly live like this, it will give us courage and patience while we fight the "good fight" (2 Timothy 4:7).

D. Christians Should Be Working

What did Paul teach Timothy about working in 2 Timothy 4:1,2? _____

_____

_____

In the parable about money in Matthew 25, the reason for using the money in the right way was that the master would come back! Turn to Luke 12:43,44. How will it be for the servant if he is found working for the master? _____

_____

_____

Remember, the Lord cannot say, "well done" if we aren't doing anything for him (Matthew 25:21,23).

Christians in every age have looked for Jesus to return. They have expected the second coming in their lifetime. This is probably the way it should be. Watching for his return moves us to live holy lives, different lives. One day Christ will come. We must be ready!

The Second Coming Of The Lord

Answer True Or False:

_____ **1.** Very little is said in the New Testament about the second coming.

_____ **2.** The Bible says the day Jesus comes again will surprise us like a thief.

_____ **3.** Christ will come by himself the second time.

_____ **4.** Only saved people will be raised at the second coming.

_____ **5.** Jesus said that only his Father knew the day or the hour he would return.

_____ **6.** Nobody has ever set a definite date for the second coming.

_____ **7.** Jesus' return will be a secret (or unseen).

_____ **8.** The Bible says that many will doubt that Jesus will come back again.

_____ **9.** Jesus will return in the clouds.

_____ **10.** There is no need to watch for Christ's return because we do not know when it will be.

Answer The Following:

1. Give three ways to be ready for the second coming:

     a. _____

     b. _____

     c. _____

2. Explain how we should live, knowing that Jesus will return. _____

_____

3. Give three proofs or witnesses of the fact of Christ's second coming:

     a. _____

     b. _____

     c. _____

4. Tell in your own words how Jesus will come back again. _____

_____